Tugs and Offshore Supply Vessels

2009/10
(UK and Ireland)

by

James Dodds

and

Bernard McCall

Introduction

This is the third edition of *Tugs and Offshore Supply Vessels - UK*. Once again, much thought has bee given to which vessels should be included. In the supply ships section will be found some vessels whic have been converted from a supply function to essentially standby vessels. Some supply shi companies have more vessels than those listed in this book; we have restricted our listing to thos vessels managed in the UK or Ireland. The tug section includes some vessels known as multicats whic are essentially workboats but with a towing capacity. There are more examples of preserved vessels i this edition. Feedback from readers of the first two editions has enabled us to decide which vessels t include. Further feedback will be much appreciated.

As with all such lists of ships, no guarantee is given about the accuracy of the figures which should b considered merely as a guideline. Every effort has been made to obtain correct figures but th disagreement among the main sources seems to have become more pronounced over the last tw years. The details are selected mainly from *Lloyd's Register of Shipping* and from company website but we emphasise that these two main sources often differ. For very new vessels, little information othe than a name is available but some of these have been included in the fleets. Information has bee corrected to the end of January 2009. The main heading for each company indicates its role a operator, owner or manager.

The details for each vessel are as follows
Column 1   Name (& flag for supply ships, followed by former names)
Column 2   Year of build
Column 3   Gross tonnage
Column 4   Length overall
Column 5   Beam
Column 6   Draught
Column 7   Horsepower
Column 8   Bollard pull ahead (n/a means not available or not applicable)

We wish to thank all the companies which have responded to requests for information, the vast majori of those listed having done so. We also wish to thank Krispen Atkinson, David Dodds, Ray Harrisor Chris Jones, Kevin Jones, Danny Lynch and Dominic McCall who have added further information, an Gilbert Mayes who has checked and corrected many details. Thanks also to the staff at Sebrigh Printers for their excellent work.

Despite our best efforts, the book may contain errors. Users of the book who have further informatio about any of the vessels listed are invited to contact us via the publisher.

James Dodds   Aberdeen   Bernard McCall   Portishead, Bristol.   March 200

Copyright © 2009 by James Dodds and Bernard McCall. The right of James Dodds and Bernarc McCall to be identified as author of this work has been asserted by them in accordance with the Copyright, Design and Patent Act 1998.

All rights reserved. No part of this publication may be reproduced, stored in a retrieval system o transmitted in any form or by any means (electronic, digital, mechanical, photocopying, recordinç or otherwise) without prior permission of the publisher.

Published by Bernard McCall, 400 Nore Road, Portishead, Bristol, BS20 8EZ, England.
Website : www.coastalshipping.co.uk
Telephone/fax : 01275 846178. E-mail : bernard@coastalshipping.co.uk
All distribution enquiries should be addressed to the publisher.

Printed by Sebright Printers, 12 - 18 Stokes Croft, Bristol, BS1 3PR
Telephone : 0117 942 5827; fax : 0117 942 0671;
e-mail : info@sebright.co.uk; website : www.sebright.co.uk

ISBN : 978-1-902953-41-0

Front cover : The WYKE CASTLE at work in Portland Bay on 1 March 2007.

(Dominic McCal

OFFSHORE VESSELS

BOSTON PUTFORD OFFSHORE SAFETY LTD

Columbus Buildings, Waveney Road, Lowestoft, Suffolk, NR32 1BN
Tel : 01502 573366   Fax : 01502 581500
E-mail : lowestoft@ckor.com
Website : www.seacormarine.com
Livery - Dark orange hull, white upperworks; black funnel with red 'S' logo.

CENTRICA PRIDE (GBR)   2007   1759   63,00   15,00   5,12   7180   85.0
(ex Seacor Easterner-07)
NOVA   (GBR)   1969   715   54,30   11,43   4,19   2400   33.0
(ex Nova Service-88; Nova Shore-80)
PUTFORD
    ACHATES   (GBR)   1976   1043   53,60   11,79   3,84   2400   n/a
(ex Maersk Tanis-89, Bin Jabr 1-87, Maersk Leader-83)
PUTFORD
    ACHILLES   (GBR)   1973   1179   58,27   13,14   5,10   4198   n/a
(ex Auriga Tide-90, Vivien Tide-84, Lady Vivien-74)
PUTFORD AJAX   (GBR)   1976   1043   53,60   11,79   3,84   2400   n/a
(ex Maersk Tanta-89, Bin Jabr 2-87, Maersk Logger-83)
PUTFORD APOLLO   (GBR)   1975   868   56,32   11,03   4,55   2310   n/a
(ex Mansal-89, Mohamed-87, Rig Mate-79)
PUTFORD ARIES   (GBR)   1977   1829   66,56   14,56   4,75   4800   n/a
(ex Stirling Aries-96, Star Aries-96)
PUTFORD ARTEMIS   (GBR)   1975   1190   58,85   12,02   4,81   6001   70.0
(ex Coral Sea 2-92, Moon Lady-90, Aomjai III-90, Selco Supply 1-87, Ibis Five-80)
PUTFORD ATHENA   (GBR)   1975   1188   58,24   12,03   4,14   6161   n/a
(ex Severn Mariner-92, Siddis Mariner-90)
PUTFORD
    ENTERPRISE   (GBR)   1985   1793   68,33   15,80   5,21   5000   n/a
(ex Stirling Altair-02, Star Altair-96)
PUTFORD
    GUARDIAN   (GBR)   1967   638   50,81   11,26   3,79   2001   n/a
(ex Essex Service-84, Essex Shore-80)
PUTFORD JAGUAR   (GBR)   2007   1759   63,00   15,00   5,12   7180   85.0
(ex Seacor Excellence-07)
PUTFORD
    PROTECTOR   (GBR)   1983   1822   68,46   16,18   5,21   4970   n/a
(ex Stirling Capella-02, Star Capella-96)
PUTFORD
    PROVIDER   (GBR)   1983   1737   68,46   16,18   5,21   4970   n/a
(ex Stirling Vega-02, Star Vega-96)
PUTFORD PUFFIN   (GBR)   1970/91   661   45,57   11,82   3,20   1440   18.0
(ex Dawn Patrol-94, Barracuda-91, Smit Barracuda-87)

Formerly used for salvage, the PUTFORD PUFFIN leaves Great Yarmouth on 16 March 200 after being repainted in drydock.

(Ashley Hunn

PUTFORD ROVER (GBR) 1982 1294 64,39 13,82 5,23 6980 84.0
(ex Al Mojil XXXIV-96, Gryphaea-93, Agip Gryphaea-89)
PUTFORD SHORE (GBR) 1967 638 48,77 10,60 3,81 1599 n/a
(ex Dawn Shore-94, Norfolk Service-84, Norfolk Shore-81)
PUTFORD SKY (GBR) 1967 459 41,38 9,86 4,13 1040 n/a
(ex Dawn Sky-94, Corella-83)
PUTFORD
   TERMINATOR (IOM) 1986 1399 65,21 14,64 5,29 5600 n/a
(ex Stirling Esk-04)
PUTFORD TRADER (GBR) 1976 1329 57,50 13,01 5,10 4200 n/a
(ex Safe Truck-95, Seaway Jura-90)
PUTFORD VIKING (GBR) 1976 1492 60,99 14,56 4,76 4800 n/a
(ex Blue Flame 1-00, Star Pegasus-87)
PUTFORD
   VOYAGER (GBR) 1985 1510 64,62 14,23 5,40 4800 n/a
(ex Stirling Dee-02)
PUTFORD WORKER (GBR) 1976 1417 65,52 14,00 5,92 3200 n/a
(ex Maersk Worker-94, Maersk Piper-85)
TYPHOON (CYM) 1976 936 56,39 11,61 3,81 2250 n/a
(ex Veesea Typhoon-00, Java Seal-91)

Offshore services in the North Sea

Part of the Seacor Group

4

BP SHIPPING OFFSHORE LTD

Farburn Industrial Estate, Dyce, Aberdeen, AB2 0PB
Tel : 01224 834836   Fax : 01224 834890
Website : www.bp.com
Livery - Black hull with two yellow stripes; white housing; red funnel with yellow lion symbol.
Managed by Vector Offshore Ltd (UK)

CALEDONIAN VANGUARD	(CYM)	2005	5729	93,60	22,00	6,50	8160	n/a
CALEDONIAN VICTORY	(CYM)	2006	5729	93,60	22,00	6,50	8160	n/a
CALEDONIAN VIGILANCE	(CYM)	2006	5729	93,60	22,00	6,50	8160	n/a
CALEDONIAN VISION	(CYM)	2006	5729	93,60	22,00	6,50	8160	n/a

Offshore services in the North Sea

BRIGGS MARINE CONTRACTORS LTD

Seaforth House, Seaforth Place, Burntisland, Fife, KY3 9AX
Tel : 01592 872939   Fax : 01592 873975
E-mail : marketing@briggsmarine.com
Website : www.briggsmarine.com
Livery - Blue hull with red and white diagnoal strip, white housing and wheelhouse with red funnel

KINGDOM OF FIFE	(GBR)	2008		61,20	13,50	4,50	5522	67.0

Marine services around Europe

BUE MARINE LTD

Imperial House, Albert Dock, Leith, EH6 7DN
Tel : 0131 554 9456   Fax : 0131 554 8328
E-mail : reception@bue.co.uk
Website : www.bue.co.uk
Livery - Dark blue hull with white housing, white funnel with company logo

CASPIAN PRIDE	(CYM)	2005	2265	71,90	16,00	6,00	5460	n/a
(ex Island Pride-07)								
CASTLE	(CYM)	1999	1969	67,00	16,00	5,91	5448	n/a
(ex Waveney Castle-02)								
CITADEL	(AZE)	2006	2050	72,00	16,00	6,00	5460	n/a
FORTRESS	(AZE)	2005	2050	72,00	16,00	6,00	5460	n/a
ISLAY	(AZE)	2002	2544	73,80	16,00	6,50	15000	170.0
(ex Stirling Islay-03)								
JURA	(AZE)	2002	2544	73,80	16,00	6,50	15000	170.0
(ex Stirling Jura-03)								
SWAN	(TKM)	1971	769	53,34	11,00	3,45	3800	n/a
(ex Hornbeck Swan-96, Seaboard Swan-95, Safe Tango-91, Nice Tango-91,								
Maersk Supporter-87)								
TULPAR	(KAZ)	2002	3343	94,08	21,00	3,96	8448	50.0

Managed for Kaspmorneftegazflot (Azerbaijan)

NEFTEGAZ 62 (AZE)	1988	2723	81,40	16,30	5,26	7200	80.0
NERCHA (AZE)	1985	3861	67,30	13,90	5,20	7240	86.0
YARENGA (AZE)	1984	1350	67,30	13,90	5,20	7150	86.0

Offshore services in the Caspian Sea

CONOCO LTD
Tetney Oil Terminal, Tetney Lock Road,Tetney, Grimsby, DN36 5NX
Tel : 01472 814101   Fax : 01469 556246

SPURN HAVEN II (GBR)	1979	654	49,80	11,60	3,39	1700	n/a

(ex Ventura-93)

Managed by Svitzer Marine Ltd

Marine services assisting shuttle tankers off Tetney monobuoy on the River Humber

DALBY OFFSHORE SERVICES LTD
Morton House, Morton Lane, Beverley, East Yorkshire, HU17 9DD
Tel : 01482 888081   Fax : 01482 888181
E-mail : info@dalbyoffshore.com
Website : www.dalbyoffshore.com

Managed for Oceanlink Management AS (Norway)

NOBLEMAN (GBR)	1989	1989	68,00	15,60	6,47	13040	140.0

(ex Far Crusader-07, Seaforth Crusader-89)

OCEAN SUPPLIER (BHS)	1984	1987	67,83	15,60	6,46	13335	145.0

(ex Norseman-08, Olympic Supplier-06, Barra Supplier-95)

OCEAN SUPPORTER (VCT)	1983	2259	71,50	16,00	6,25	10880	124.0

(ex Anchorman-08, Misr Gulf VII-06, Maersk Trinity-05, Maersk Handler-02,
Maersk Supporter-98, Mahone Bay-87)

ROMAN (IOM)	1983	1971	68,00	15,60	6,45	13040	141.0

(ex Far Centurion-07, Seaforth Centurion-89)

STATESMAN (GBR)	1976	1976	78,00	14,03	6,12	9460	132.0

(ex Sun Wrestler-99, Baru-91, Schoorturm-87)

Offshore services worldwide

DOF (UK) LTD
Voyager House, 75 Waterloo Quay, Aberdeen, AB11 5DE
Tel : 01224 586644   Fax : 01224 586555
E-mail : info@dofman.co.uk
Website : www.dof.no
Livery - Red hull, white housing with blue horizontal stripes and white funnel with comany
logo

SKANDI BARRA (NOR)	2005	3350	86,00	19,70		5984	n/a

Managed for DOF ASA (Norway)

SKANDI CARLA	(BHS)	2001	4456	83,85	19,70	6,10	13404	n/a
SKANDI FOULA	(NOR)	2002	3252	83,85	19,70	5,85	8208	n/a
SKANDI RONA	(NIS)	2002	3252	83,85	19,70	5,85	8208	n/a

Offshore services worldwide

EDDA SUPPLY SHIPS (UK) LTD
3rd Floor, Salvesen Tower, Blaikies Quay, Aberdeen, AB11 5BW
Tel : 01224 587788   Fax : 01224 583276
E-mail : info@eddasupplyships.com
Livery - Orange hull with dark yellow housing and wheelhouse
   Managed for Østensjø Rederi AS

EDDA FRAM	(NOR)	2007	3706	85,80	19,40	6,70	10336	n/a

Offshore services worldwide

The EDDA FRAM arrives at Aberdeen on 8 February 2008.

(Barry Standerline)

ESVAGT A/S
Maersk House, Crawpeel Road, Altens, Aberdeen, AB12 3LG
Tel : 01224 243431
E-mail : abz@esvagt.co.uk
Website : www.esvagt.dk
Livery - Red hull with 'Esvagt' in black lettering and red housing

ESVAGT CAPELLA	(DIS)	2004	922	44,03	11,50	4,24	2720	15.0
ESVAGT DEE	(IOM)	2000	1863	56,64	14,60	6,01	6526	95.0
(ex Maersk Dee-07)								

ESVAGT DON (IOM)	2000	1863	56,64	14,60	6,00	6526	95.0
(ex Maersk Don-06)							
ESVAGT OBSERVER (DIS)	2000	1863	56,64	14,60	6,02	6526	95.0
ESVAGT SUPPORTER (DIS)	1989	723	41,90	9,10	5,00	2500	20.0
(ex Torland 1-01, Torland-00)							

Offshore services worldwide
Part of the A P Møller - Mærsk Group

FARSTAD SHIPPING LTD
Farstad House, Badentoy Avenue, Badentoy Park, Portlethen, Aberdeen, AB12 4YB
Tel : 01224 784000   Fax : 01224 783340
E-mail : aberdeen@farstad.co.uk
Website : www.farstad.no
Livery - Red hull with large white 'F' and white housing

FAR GRIMSHADER (IOM)	1983	2528	80,85	17,52	5,00	12240	n/a
(ex Loch Grimshader-90, Far Scandia-87, Stad Scandia-86)							
FAR SABRE (IOM)	2008	3050	79,80	17,20	6,80	14400	150.0
FAR SCIMITAR (IOM)	2008	3089	79,80	17,20	6,80		150.0
FAR SCOTIA (IOM)	2001	1989	67,00	16,00	5,90	5378	n/a
FAR SERVICE (IOM)	1995	3052	83,80	18,80	6,35	7200	n/a
FAR SPIRIT (IOM)	2007	2451	73,40	16,60	6,40	6528	n/a
FAR STRIDER (IOM)	1999	3009	82,85	19,00	6,33	6700	n/a
FAR SUPERIOR (IOM)	1990	2999	81,90	18,01	4,97	6600	n/a
FAR SUPPLIER (IOM)	1999	3009	82,85	19,05	6,33	6700	n/a
FAR SUPPORTER (IOM)	1996	2998	83,80	18,80	6,20	7200	n/a

Offshore services worldwide

GULF OFFSHORE NORTH SEA LTD
184 - 192 Market Street, Aberdeen, AB11 5PQ
Tel : 01224 336000   Fax : 01224 336039
E-mail : steve.wilson@gulfoffshore.co.uk
Website : www.gulfmark.com
Livery - Dark blue hull with white housing and white funnel with company logo.
         Orange hull with white housing (Fratelli D'Amato vessels)
         Dark green hull with white housing (Rim. Napolitani vessels)

CLWYD SUPPORTER (GBR)	1984	2762	81,39	16,30	4,91	7200	78.0
(ex Neftegaz-12-95)							
HIGHLAND tbn	2009		86,60	19,00	5,90	4850	n/a
HIGHLAND BUGLER (GBR)	2002	1992	67,70	16,00	5,90	5450	n/a
HIGHLAND CHAMPION (GBR)	1979	2501	81,08	18,04	4,32	4800	n/a
(ex Balblair-93, Tender Champion-85)							

HIGHLAND CITADEL (GBR) (ex Waveney Citadel-04)	2003	2161	72,70	16,00	5,82	5452	n/a
HIGHLAND COURAGE (GBR)	2002	3160	80,00	18,00	6,60	16320	170.0
HIGHLAND DRUMMER (PAN)	1997	1969	67,00	16,00	5,91	5450	n/a
HIGHLAND EAGLE (GBR)	2003	2244	72,00	16,00	5,91	5460	n/a
HIGHLAND ENDURANCE (GBR)	2003	3160	80,00	18,00	6,60	16320	170.0
HIGHLAND FORTRESS (GBR)	2001	2244	71,80	16,00	5,90	5450	n/a
HIGHLAND LEGEND (GBR) (ex Wimpey Seawitch-88)	1986	1001	59,00	13,11	4,40	3589	n/a
HIGHLAND MONARCH (GBR)	2003	1992	67,70	16,00	5,90	5438	n/a
HIGHLAND NAVIGATOR (GBR)	2002	3227	84,00	18,80	6,20	9598	n/a
HIGHLAND PIONEER (GBR) (ex Oceanic Pioneer-00, Lowland Pioneer-99, Balder Vigra-85)	1983	2099	68,51	17,84	4,90	5982	n/a
HIGHLAND PIPER (GBR)	1996	1969	67,00	16,80	5,90	5450	n/a
HIGHLAND PRESTIGE (GBR)	2007	3702	88,00	19,00	5,90	4850	n/a

Viewed from the north side of the harbour entrance, the HIGHLAND PRESTIGE arrives at Aberdeen on 17 July 2007.

(David Dodds)

HIGHLAND PRIDE (GBR)	1992	2610	81,90	18,00	4,98	6602	n/a
HIGHLAND ROVER (GBR)	1998	2186	71,80	16,00	5,90	5460	n/a
HIGHLAND SPIRIT (GBR)	1998	1717	61,60	17,80	5,60	5954	80.0
HIGHLAND SPRITE (GBR)	1986	1199	59,21	14,13	4,40	3589	n/a
(ex Wimpey Seasprite-88)							
HIGHLAND STAR (GBR)	1991	2637	81,90	18,00	4,98	6602	n/a
(ex Far Malin-91)							
HIGHLAND							
TRADER (GBR)	1996	1969	67,00	16,00	5,91	5450	n/a
(ex Safe Truck-06)							
HIGHLAND							
VALOUR (GBR)	2003	3160	80,00	18,00	6,60	16320	180.0
HIGHLAND							
WARRIOR (GBR)	1981	2960	81,80	18,00	5,76	5300	n/a
(ex Atlantic Warrior-97, Wira Maju-91, Stad Flex-88)							
SEFTON							
SUPPORTER (GBR)	1971	1219	76,26	12,25	3,32	1620	n/a
(ex Marpol Fighter-95, Al Waasit-92, Marpol Fighter-90, Al Waasit-88, Norskjell Nor-87,							
Norskjell-85)							
Managed for Fratelli D'Amato SpA (Italy)							
F. D. INCREDIBLE (GBR)	2007	2305	72,00	16,00	5,90	5460	n/a
F. D. INVINCIBLE (GBR)	2006	2305	72,00	16,00	5,90	5460	n/a
F. D. IRRESISTIBLE (GBR)	2008	2305	72,00	16,00	5,90	5460	n/a
F. D. RELIABLE (GBR)	2007	2305	72,00	16,00	5,90	5460	n/a

Although only recently delivered, paint is flaking off the bow of the F. D. RELIABLE as she leaves Great Yarmouth and heads for Den Helder on 9 December 2007.
(Ashley Hunn)

(tbn) (GBR)	2010		86,60	19,00	5,90		4850	n/a
GARGANO (GBR)	2002	2244	72,00	16,00			5452	n/a
PORTOSALVO (GBR)	2005	2154	72,00	16,00	5,90		5480	n/a

Offshore services in the North Sea and Irish Sea

IRISH MAINPORT HOLDINGS
Mainport, Monahan Road, Cork, Republic of Ireland
Tel : +353 21 4317900   Fax : +353 21 4317111
E-mail : info@mainport.ie
Website : www.mainport.ie
Livery - Dark blue hull with white housing
   Managed by Mainport Ireland (Ireland)

MAINPORT ASH (MHL)	1982	1089	57,45	12,50	4,80	4500	60.0
(ex Smit-Lloyd 25-06)							
MAINPORT ELM (MHL)	1983	1089	57,46	12,53	4,81	4562	60.0
(ex Moray-07, Smit-Lloyd 31-00)							
MAINPORT OAK (MHL)	1983	1089	57,46	12,21	4,81	4500	60.0
(ex Smit-Lloyd 32-06)							

   Managed by Seahorse Ltd (Ireland)

PEARL (IRL)	1986	1296	65,36	13,09	4,59	6100	70.0
(ex Veesea Pearl-00, Droit De Parole-94, Cariboo-93, Fort Reliance-89)							
SEAHORSE SUPPORTER (IRL)	1974	692	52,68	11,66	4,05	3000	n/a
(ex Wendentor-90)							

Offshore services off the south east coast of Ireland
Part of Mainport Group

KLYNE TUGS LOWESTOFT LTD
Cumberland Place, Whapload Road Lowestoft, Suffolk, NR32 1UQ
Tel : 01502 515250   Fax : 01502 500225
E-mail : Enquiries@klyne-tugs.co.uk
Website: www.jpknight.com
Livery - Green hull with buff housing

ANGLIAN EARL (BRB)	1987	2311	69,90	15,90	6,50	12000	135.0
(ex Maersk Logger-03)							

Offshore services and reliefs for MCA coastguard tugs
Now part of the J P Knight Group and trading as J P Knight (Anglian) Ltd

MAERSK SUPPLY SERVICE
Maersk House, Crawpeel Road, Altens, Aberdeen, AB12 3LG
Tel : 01224 243241
E-mail : abzmss@maersk.com
Website : www.maersksupplyservice.com
Livery - Sky blue hull with buff housing and wheelhouse

The Aberdeen pilot boat is dwarfed by the huge bulk of the MAERSK ADVANCER as she leaves Aberdeen on 12 July 2008.

(Barry Standerline)

MAERSK ADVANCER (IOM)	2004	6536	90,30	23,00	7,80	23500	280.0
MAERSK ASSERTER (IOM)	2004	6536	90,30	23,00	7,80	23500	280.0
MAERSK BEATER (IOM)	1997	4393	82,20	19,80	7,50	20020	237.0
MAERSK CUTTER (IOM)	1983	1972	68,84	15,55	6,40	14400	182.0
MAERSK FINDER (IOM)	1994	2961	82,50	18,80	6,24	7200	n/a
MAERSK HANDLER (IOM)	2002	2000	80,00	18,00	6,59	17500	198.0
MAERSK HELPER (IOM)	2002	2000	80,00	18,00	6,59	17500	198.0
MAERSK MARINER (GBR)	1986	3949	82,00	18,40	6,90	14900	170.0
MAERSK RETRIEVER (GBR)	1979	1894	67,11	15,50	6,46	13000	152.0
MAERSK RIDER (GBR)	1982	1894	67,00	15,50	6,46	14400	181.0
MAERSK ROVER (GBR)	1982	1894	67,00	15,50	6,46	14400	161.0
MAERSK SEARCHER (IOM)	1999	4140	72,00	18,80	7,50	18250	200.0
MAERSK SERVER (IOM)	2000	4013	72,00	18,80	7,50	18250	200.0
MAERSK SHIPPER (IOM)	1999	4013	72,00	18,80	7,50	18250	200.0
MAERSK SUPPORTER (IOM)	1999	4013	72,00	18,80	7,50	18250	214.0

Offshore services worldwide

NOMIS SHIPPING LTD

Links Place, Aberdeen, AB11 5DY
Tel : 01224 569800   Fax : 01224 569801
E-mail : Aberdeen@nomisshipping.com
Website : www.nomisshipping.com
Livery - Black, dark blue or orange hull with white housing and bright yellow funnel

Name	Flag	Year							
ABERDONIAN	(GBR)	1977	480	44,75	10,82	4,95	3000	n/a
(ex Starmi-89)								
DEA ARGOSY	(BHS)	1999	1402	61,00	13,80	4,90	5300	68.0
(ex Seacor Argosy-03)								
DEA CHALLENGER	(BHS)	1975/90	1217	58,76	12,02	4,81	6000	70.0
(ex Asia Maru-98, Aomjai 2-90, Selco Supply II-87, Ibis Six-80)								
DEA CHAMPION	(BHS)	1980	1235	60,36	14,00	5,01	6000	80.0
(ex Smit-Lloyd 71-98)								
DEA CLIPPER	(BRB)	1981/07	713	56,39	12,20	3,66	3000	n/a
(ex Landry Tide-07, Petromar General-93)								
DEA CONQUEROR	(BHS)	1982	1236	60,48	14,00	5,25	6000	80.0
(ex Smit-Lloyd 73-98)								
DEA HERCULES	(BHS)	2007	1690	59,25	14,95	4,95	5150	65.8
DEA LINGUE	(VCT)	1972	786	54,81	12,30	4,97	4000	43.0
(ex Lingue-04, Smit-Lloyd 41-85)								
DEA OCEAN	(BRB)	1983/06	782	55,00	12,19	4,50	2250	30.0
(ex Needham Tide-05)								
DEA ODYSSEY	(BHS)	1987	1256	58,04	13,50	5,06	5331	67.0
(ex Smit-Lloyd 57-04)								
DEA PILOT	(GBR)	1973	950	56,39	12,15	4,55	4078	n/a
(ex Rossinant-94, Kentonvale Star-92, Bass Tide-87, Bass Shore-79)								
DEA PROTECTOR	(GBR)	1974	1104	58,94	11,92	3,79	2000	n/a
(ex Scott Protector-04, Normand Carrier-89)								
DEA SAILOR	(BHS)	1981	516	39,62	8,86	3,36	1700	20.0
(ex Toisa Widgeon-04, Canmar Widgeon-90)								
DEA SCOUT	(BHS)	1981	516	39,62	8,86	3,36	1700	20.0
(ex Toisa Teal-04, Canmar Teal-90)								
DEA SEARCHER	(BHS)	1983	516	39,62	12,19	3,67	2250	30.0
(ex Toisa Petrel-03, Lynn Pelham-91)								
DEA SEEKER	(BHS)	1979	782	56,54	11,58	4,27	2250	n/a
(ex Toisa Puffin-04, Marsea One-91)								
DEA SERVER	(BHS)	1979	863	56,54	11,58	3,70	2250	30.0
(ex Toisa Plover-03, Veesea-91, Kara Seal-91)								
DEA SUPPORTER	(IOM)	1970	950	51,70	11,59	4,20	5750	n/a
(ex Mastodon-91)								
DEA ZEUS	(BRB)	2007	1690	59,25	14,95	4,95	5150	65.0

Towage and offshore services worldwide

Company has been taken over by Vroon Offshore Services. It has been announced that vessels will be repainted in Vroon livery and renamed.

A fine low angle view of the DEA SAILOR approaching Aberdeen on 29 September 2007.

(David Dodds)

NORTH STAR SHIPPING LTD
207 Albert Quay, Aberdeen, AB11 5FS
Tel : 01224 592206   Fax : 01224 584174
E-mail : info@craig-group.com
Website : www.craig-group.com
Livery - Dark orange hull with buff housing, red/grey/black striped funnel.

GRAMPIAN tbn	(GBR)	2009	2950	78,20	17,00	5,50	5600	n/a
GRAMPIAN tbn	(GBR)	2010		60,00	16,00			90.0
GRAMPIAN CAVALIER	(GBR)	2007	125	48,25	11,00	4,25	1900	n/a
GRAMPIAN COMMANDER	(GBR)	2005	1125	48,25	11,00	4,25	1900	n/a
GRAMPIAN CONQUEROR	(GBR)	2006	11,25	48,25	11,00	4,25	1900	n/a
GRAMPIAN CONQUEST	(GBR)	2006	1125	48,25	11,00	4,25	1900	n/a
GRAMPIAN CONTENDER	(GBR)	2006	1125	48,25	11,00	4,25	1900	n/a
GRAMPIAN CORSAIR	(GBR)	2007	1125	48,25	11,00	4,25	1900	n/a
GRAMPIAN COURAGEOUS	(GBR)	2006	1125	48,25	11,00	4,25	1900	n/a
GRAMPIAN CRUSADER	(GBR)	1976	1450	61,00	13,80	5,13	4200	n/a

(ex Hamilton Piper-92, Hamilton Piper 1-90, Hamilton Piper-87)

The GRAMPIAN CORSAIR leaves Aberdeen on 31 May 2008.

(Barry Standerline)

GRAMPIAN DEE (GBR)   1975   419   35,00   9,44   4,75   1448   n/a
(ex Drot-90, Boston Halifax-86)
GRAMPIAN
   DEFENDER (GBR)   2002   800   47,10   11,10   5,80   2460   n/a
(ex BUE Westray-04)
GRAMPIAN
   EXPLORER (GBR)   2003   2244   71,80   16,00   5,90   5460   n/a
GRAMPIAN FALCON (GBR) 1981   769   52,00   11,00   4,70   1300   n/a
(ex Burnhaven-90, Stirling Imp-87)
GRAMPIAN FAME (GBR)   1975   1380   65,00   14,00   5,90   3200   n/a
(ex Red Sea Trader-92, Maersk Pacer-87)
GRAMPIAN
   FRONTIER (GBR)   1997   2064   69,90   14,50   5,51   8300   100.0
GRAMPIAN
   GUARDIAN (GBR)   1980   1112   55,00   12,20   4,50   3486   n/a
(ex Amazon Guardian-00, Grampian Guardian-00, Atlantic Guardian-98,
   Big Orange XV-91)
GRAMPIAN HAVEN (GBR) 1982   591   52,00   11,00   4,70   1300   n/a
(ex Portnahaven-90, Stirling Merlin-89)
GRAMPIAN
   HIGHLANDER (GBR)   1975   1547   60,00   13,80   5,12   4200   n/a
(ex City of Aberdeen-90, Polar Fjord-90, Normand Providence-86, Stad Scandia-81)
GRAMPIAN
   HUNTER (GBR)   1992   763   47,00   10,00   4,90   2135   n/a

Name		Year							
GRAMPIAN ORCADES	(GBR)	1991	763	47,00	10,00	4,90	2135	n/a
GRAMPIAN OSPREY	(GBR)	1979	905	61,00	11,60	4,65	3200	n/a
(ex Sea Serv Osprey-96, Stirling Osprey-93)								
GRAMPIAN OTTER	(GBR)	1983	625	52,00	11,00	4,70	1400	n/a
(ex Johnshaven-90, Stirling Elf-88)								
GRAMPIAN PIONEER	(GBR)	1981	501	40,00	10,00	5,80	1374	n/a
(ex Standby Pioneer-84)								
GRAMPIAN PRIDE	(GBR)	1981	501	40,00	10,04	5,80	1374	n/a
(ex Standby Pride-83)								
GRAMPIAN PRINCE	(GBR)	1984	1294	65,00	13,80	5,21	6000	80.0
(ex Al Mojil 35-96, Bellerophon-93, Agip Bellerophon-89)								
GRAMPIAN PROTECTOR	(GBR)	1983	573	45,00	10,00	6,00	1950	n/a
(ex Standby Protector-86)								
GRAMPIAN RANGER	(GBR)	2002	800	47,10	11,00	5,80	2460	n/a
(ex BUE Stronsay-04)								
GRAMPIAN SPRITE	(GBR)	1982	766	52,00	11,00	4,70	1300	n/a
(ex Stirling Sprite-90)								
GRAMPIAN STAR	(GBR)	1988	560	45,00	9,20	5,41	1500	n/a
(ex North Safe-88, Rollanes-84)								
GRAMPIAN SURVEYOR	(GBR)	2003	2786	75,00	16,00	5,25	5982	n/a
GRAMPIAN TALISMAN	(GBR)	2007	2950	78,20	17,00	5,50	5600	n/a
GRAMPIAN VENTURE	(GBR)	1981	766	52,00	11,00	4,70	1300	n/a
(ex Sandhaven-90, Stirling Puck-87)								

Offshore services in the North Sea

Part of the Craig Group

OCEAN MAINPORT OFFSHORE LTD
Mainport, Monahan Road, Cork, Republic of Ireland
Tel : +353 21 4317900   Fax : +353 21 4317111
E-mail : info@mainport.ie
Website : www.mainport.ie
Livery - Red hull with white housing and funnel

Managed by Sartor Shipping Ltd (Norway)

Name		Year							
OCEAN FIGHTER	(NOR)	1980	891	61,24	11,84	4,01	3200	n/a
(ex Stirling Tern-97)								
OCEAN PRINCE	(NOR)	1976	1322	64,54	13,83	4,72	7040	99.0
(ex Viking Prince-05, Stad Supplier-89)								
OCEAN SKY	(NOR)	1975	1314	64,55	13,83	3,23	7040	99.0
(ex Pan Sky-95, Far Sky-90, Stad Sky-86)								

OCEAN SPIRIT (NIS)   1983   2169   69,09   17,51   5,02   6120   n/a
(ex Far Spirit-05, Loch Shuna-89, Far Spirit-87, Stad Spirit-86)
OCEAN VIKING (NOR)   1986   2090   69,30   15,50   5,71   6000   n/a
(ex Viking Fighter-05, Tender Fighter-91)
OCEAN VISCOUNT (GBR) 1971   604   46,69   9,02   4,49   1200   n/a
(ex Viking Viscount-06, Cam Viscount-95, Raiti-91)
OCEAN WEST (NOR)   1974   1104   58,72   11,52   3,81   2100   n/a
(ex Siggbas-05, West Plover-85)
SARTOR (NOR)   1976   2019   67,80   17,33   4,62   4200   n/a
(ex Northern Viking-04, Veronica Viking-97, Sealion Columbia-90, Active Duke-84)
Offshore services in the North Sea

Part of Mainport Group

The SARTOR leaves Great Yarmouth on 19 November 2006.

(Ashley Hunn)

OCEAN MAINPORT RESCUE LTD

Merchants House, 87 Waterloo Quay, Aberdeen, AB11 5DE
Tel : 01224 212159   Fax : 01224 211513
E-mail : operations@oceanmainport.co.uk
Website : www.oceanmainport.com
Livery - Red hull with white housing and funnel
OCEAN CLEVER (GBR)   1975   1409   71,37   12,37   4,44   7040 150.0
(ex Havila Clever-07, Kronbas-98, West Penguin-86, Atlantic Fosna-80, Edda Atlantic-76)
OCEAN NESS (BHS)   2001   1864   66,00   15,00   4,70   5434   n/a
(ex Havila Tigris-07)

OCEAN SEARCHER   (BHS) 1975   1472   64,40   13,80   5,90   8000   105.0
(ex Havila Searcher-07, Rem Searcher-98, Plan Searcher-95, Pan Searcher-93,
  Far Searcher-90, Tender Searcher-87)
OCEAN SPEY   (BHS)   2000   1864   66,00   15,00   4,70   5434   n/a
(ex Havila Star-07)
OCEAN SPRITE   (BHS)   1975   1499   61,20   13,86   5,10   4200   n/a
(ex Havila Sea-07, Emerald Bas-98, Emerald Sprite-92, Sprite-91, Edda Sprite-83)
OCEAN SUN   (BHS)   1972   1151   58,40   11,70   4,35   2850   n/a
(ex Havila Sun-07, Sunbas-98, Sun Tender-95, North Breeze-91, Ocean Range-90,
  Rembertiturm-88)
OCEAN SWAN   (GBR)   1983   488   52,00   12,50   4,10   1600   n/a
(ex Amilcar-07)
OCEAN SWIFT   (GBR)   1957/85 579   56,74   9,35   4,50   2300   n/a
(ex Havila Sky-07, Rescue Kim-98, Kim-95, Rescue Kim-91, Andenes-84, R 5-65)
OCEAN TERN   (GBR)   1974   1104   58,72   11,52   4,20   1860   n/a
(ex Havila Tern-07, Rescue Tern-98, West Tern-85)
Offshore services in the North Sea

SBS MARINE LTD
Old Stoneywood Church, Bankhead Road, Bucksburn, Aberdeen, AB21 9HQ
Tel : 01224 712277   Fax : 01224 716987
E-mail : info@sbsmarine.com
Website : www.sbsmarine.com
Livery - Black hull, white housing and red funnel with white band
SBS CIRRUS   (GBR)   1985   2562   80,78   18,00   4,96   6120   n/a
(ex Active Duke-01)
SBS NIMBUS   (GBR)   2003   2596   73,40   16,60   6,50   5520   n/a
SBS STRATUS   (GBR)   2003   2596   73,40   16,60   6,50   5520   n/a
SBS TEMPEST   (GBR)   2006   2596   73,40   16,60   6,40   5520   n/a
SBS TORRENT   (GBR)   2007   2599   73,40   16,60   6,40   5520   n/a
SBS TYPHOON   (GBR)   2006   2465   73,40   16,60   6,40   5520   n/a
Offshore supply services in the North Sea
Part of the Kistefos Group

SEALION SHIPPING LTD
Gostrey House, Union Road, Farnham, Surrey, GU9 7PT
Tel : 01252 737773   Fax : 01252 737770
E-mail : info@sealionshipping.co.uk
Website : www.sealionshipping.co.uk
Livery - Orange hull with buff housing and wheelhouse, buff funnel with company badge
TOISA tbn   (BHS)   2010   83,00   20,00   18800   210.0
TOISA tbn   (BHS)   2011   83,00   20,00   18800   210.0
TOISA tbn   (BHS)   2011   87,40   19,00   6,65   8200   n/a
TOISA tbn   (BHS)   2011   83,00   20,00   18800   210.0
TOISA tbn   (BHS)   2011   87,40   19,00   6,65   8200   n/a
TOISA
    CONQUEROR   (GBR)   2001   2401   73,80   16,05   6,28   5228   n/a

TOISA CORAL (GBR)	1999	2401	73,80	16,05	6,33	5228	n/a
TOISA CREST (GBR)	1999	2401	73,80	16,05	6,29	5228	n/a
TOISA DARING (BHS)	2006	2765	69,00	16,60	6,20	12236	160.0
TOISA DAUNTLESS (BHS)	2006	2765	69,00	16,60	6,20	12236	160.0
TOISA DEFIANT (BHS)	2006	2765	69,00	16,60	6,20	12236	160.0
TOISA INDEPENDENT (GBR)	2003	3100	83,20	19,05	5,92	7341	n/a
TOISA INTREPID (BHS)	1998	2990	82,85	19,05	6,34	6688	n/a
TOISA INVINCIBLE (BHS)	1998	2990	82,85	19,05	6,32	6688	n/a
TOISA LEOPARD (PAN) (ex TNT Leopard-90)	1983	846	61,73	11,84	4,00	3200	n/a
TOISA LION (BHS) (ex TNT Lion-90)	1983	846	61,73	11,84	4,02	3200	n/a
TOISA PALADIN (GBR)	2008	5648	103,70	19,74	6,14	12750	n/a
TOISA SERENADE (BHS)	2008	3390	87,40	19,00	6,65	8200	n/a
TOISA SOLITAIRE (BHS)	2008	3390	87,40	19,00	6,65	8200	n/a
TOISA SONATA (BHS)	2008	3390	87,40	19,00	6,65	8200	n/a
TOISA TIGER (BHS) (ex TNT Tiger-90)	1983	846	61,73	11,84	4,00	3520	n/a
TOISA VALIANT (BHS)	2005	3406	80,50	18,00	6,10	7178	n/a
TOISA VIGILANT (BHS)	2005	3406	80,50	18,00	6,10	7178	n/a
TOISA VOYAGER (BHS)	2005	3404	80,50	18,00	6,10	7178	n/a

Also operate diving support vessels

Offshore services worldwide

The TOISA INDEPENDENT leaves Aberdeen in dramatic evening light on 7 August 2006.

(Barry Standerline)

SOLSTAD OFFSHORE (UK) LTD

3rd Floor, Salvesen Tower, Blaikies Quay, Aberdeen, AB11 5PW
Tel : 01224 560280   Fax : 012224 560821
E-mail : office@solstad.co.uk
Website : www.solstad.co.uk
Livery - Orange hull, white housing & wheelhouse. Buff funnel with company badge.

Managed for Solstad Shipping AS (Norway)

NORMAND AURORA	(NOR)	2005	3739	86,20	19,16	6,65	10196	n/a
NORMAND CLIPPER	(NOR)	2001/05	12291	127,50	23,40	8,60	22838	120.0
NORMAND CUTTER	(IOM)	2001/06	12291	127,50	23,40	8,40	22838	120.0
NORMAND FLIPPER	(NOR)	2003	3396	88,60	18,80	6,20	10340	n/a
NORMAND INSTALLER	(NIS)	2006	14506	123,65	28,00	8,30	31326	275.0
NORMAND JARL	(NOR)	1984	2686	75,50	16,60	5,60	12000	148.0
NORMAND MARINER	(NOR)	2002	4462	82,10	20,00	7,51	23500	270.0

Although there are offshore installations in the Irish Sea, the vast majority of supply and suppo
ship movements are at ports on the east coast of the UK to support work in the North Sea oil an
gas fields. The vast majority of photographs submitted for possible inclusion in this section of th
book were taken at Aberdeen or Great Yarmouth. Making a welcome change, the NORMAN
MARINER arrives on the River Tyne on 21 June 2007.

(Dominic McCa

NORMAND								
MJOLNE	(NOR)	1985	3385	83,55	18,00	5,57	17932	175.0
NORMAND								
NEPTUN	(NOR)	1996	3663	80,40	18,46	7,77	18192	220.0
NORMAND								
PIONEER	(IOM)	1999	5913	95,00	24,00	8,23	25124	286.0
NORMAND								
TONJER	(IOM)	1983	3349	80,77	18,00	4,30	6000	n/a
NORMAND								
VESTER	(NOR)	1998	3061	84,38	18,80	6,25	9100	n/a

Offshore services worldwide

TRICO SUPPLY (UK) LTD
14 Albyn Terrace, Aberdeen, AB10 1YP
Tel : 01224 633366   Fax : 01224 630818
Website : www.tricomarine.com
Livery - Dark red hull with cream housing and funnel
Managed for Trico Supply AS (Norway)

NORTHERN								
CANYON	(BHS)	2002	3500	85,25	18,80		10662	n/a
NORTHERN								
CHASER	(DMA)	1991	2335	73,60	16,40	6,80	15612	166.0

(ex Andrew Viking-97)

The crew of the NORTHERN MARINER, arriving at Aberdeen on 24 December 2006, will hope to spend the Christmas season in port.

(David Dodds)

NORTHERN
MARINER (DMA) 1986 1532 60,20 14,40 5,70 3190 n/a
(ex Suffolk Mariner-97)
NORTHERN QUEEN (GBR) 1982 1833 67,20 16,80 6,08 6880 n/a
(ex Mona Viking-97, Sea Guardian-90, Sea Worker-84)
NORTHERN
SUPPORTER (GBR) 1996 1969 67,00 16,00 5,91 5448 n/a
(ex Suffolk Supporter-97)
Offshore services in the North Sea
Part of Trico Marine Group

VROON OFFSHORE SERVICES LIMITED
4th Floor, Regent Center, Regent Road, Aberdeen, AB11 5NS
Tel : 01224 578750   Fax : 01224 578751
E-mail : info@uk.vroonoffshore.com
Website : www.uk.vroonoffshore.com
Livery - Orange hull with large white 'V' and white housing
VIKING DEFENDER (GBR) 1983 680 46,82 11,02 6,91 2760 n/a
(ex Cam Defender-95, Jagima-88)
VIKING EXPLORER (GBR) 2007 1544 55,20 12,70 4,65 2011 n/a

As the former ships of BUE Marine are renamed to fit in with the Vroon naming system, so de they lose their distinctive black and yellow livery which is displayed to good effect by the VIKINC EXPLORER as she arrives at Aberdeen on 21 May 2007.

(Barry Standerline

VIKING IONA (GBR)   1977   1393   61,00   13,80   5,13   4200   n/a
(ex BUE Iona-07, Coral-99, Hornbeck Coral-96, Seaboard Coral-95, Boa Coral-92,
    Ocean Coral-90, Highland Piper 1-87, Highland Piper-87)
VIKING PROVIDER (GBR)   1999   2102   68,13   14,50   5,66   6526   63.0
VIKING RANGER (GBR)   1983   680   46,72   11,61   6,92   2330   n/a
(ex Cam Ranger-95, Sentinel Cathinka-88)
VIKING SENTINEL (GBR)   1982   673   46,72   10,24   6,75   2250   n/a
(ex Cam Sentinel-95, Sentinel Maria-87)
VOS CANNA (GBR)   1980   836   55,40   11,60   3,97   2480   n/a
(ex BUE Canna-07, Sapphire Tide-99, Hornbeck Sapphire-96, Seaboard Sapphire-95,
    Sape-90)
VOS CHANCELLOR (VCT) 1973/01 934   59,54   12,25   4,81   6160   72.0
(ex Dea Chancellor-08, Chain Supplier-01, Bon Valor-98, Royal-86, Jason-80,
    Stella Salvator-77)
VOS COMMANDER (GBR)   1975   497   58,95   12,00   4,10   1152   70.0
(ex Dea Commander-08, Normand Gard-96, Normand Conger-85, Normand Vibran-81,
    Ocean Pilot-79, Normand Vibran-76)
VOS CONQUEST (GBR)   1974   422   39,80   8,95   3,94   2000   n/a
(ex Britannia Conquest-09, Suffolk Conquest-91)
VOS CRUSADER (GBR)   1975/91 1176   59,98   12,01   4,15   6160   55.0
(ex Viking Crusader-08, Britannia Crusader-97, Pan Salvor-91, Gute Salvor-90,
    Normand Engineer-87)
VOS DISCOVERY (GBR)   2007   1544   55,20   12,70   4,65   2011   n/a
(ex Viking Discovery-09)
VOS EMPEROR (GBR)   1977   624   37,95   9,83   4,55   1281   n/a
(ex Black Watch-09, Kaskazi-91)
VOS FIGHTER (GBR)   1973   1022   53,15   11,74   4,20   5600   n/a
(ex Dea Fighter-09, Sea Sapphire-92, Ibis Two-81)
VOS GUARDIAN (GBR)   1993   1280   55,00   12,70   4,50   1218   n/a
(ex Viking Guardian-08, Scott Guardian-05)
VOS HARVESTER (GBR)   1972   430   39,80   8,95   3,94   2000   n/a
(ex Britannia Harvester-09, Suffolk Harvester-90, Venturer-84, Suffolk Harvester-79)
VOS HUNTER (GBR)   1979   1317   64,83   14,10   4,70   7100   113.0
(ex Dea Hunter-09, Triumph Sea-01, Acadian Mistral-01, Offshore Hunter-86,
    Kongsholm-84, Normand Hunter-84)
VOS INNOVATOR (GBR)   2007   1544   55,20   12,70   4,65   2011   n/a
VOS INSPIRER (GBR)   2007   1544   55,20   12,70   4,65   2011   n/a
VOS ISLAY (GBR)   1985/91 928   53,00   12,00   4,62   3808   48.0
(ex Viking Islay-08, BUE Islay-05, Searcher-99, Hornbeck Searcher-96,
    Sunset Searcher-95, Far Searcher-93, Nuna-91)
VOS LISMORE (IOM)   1986   977   53,85   12,22   4,71   2023   n/a
(ex BUE Lismore-07, Baronet-99, Hornbeck Baronet-96, Sunset Baronet-95,
    Far Baronet-93, Seaforth Baronet-89)
VOS MARINER (GBR)   1975   846   53,22   11,03   3,46   4600   n/a
(ex Dea Mariner-08, ODS Manta-93, Adil-86, Nor Truck-81)
VOS MASTER (IOM)   1993   1607   66,40   14,00   5,10   7260   95.0
(ex Caledonia Master-08, Artabaze-96)

VOS MONARCH   (GBR)   1973   422   39,80   8,95   3,94   2000   n/a
(ex Britannia Monarch-09, Suffolk Monarch-90, St David-84, Suffok Monarch-78)
VOS MULL   (GBR)   1980   844   55,66   11,60   3,99   2480   n/a
(ex Viking Mull-07, BUE Mull-05, Sceptre Tide-99, Hornbeck Sceptre-98,
   Seaboard Sceptre-95, Salgado-90)
VOS OLYMPIAN   (BHS)   2006   1772   62,95   14,95   5,00   5500   68.0
(ex Dea Olympian-09)
VOS PATHFINDER   (GBR)   2008   1544   55,20   12,70   4,65   2011   n/a
VOS PATROL   (BRB)   1982/07 804   54,87   12,19   3,66   2536   n/a
(ex Dea Patrol-08, Estay Tide-06)
VOS PIONEER   (GBR)   2008   1544   60,20   12,70   4,65   2011   n/a
VOS PRINCE   (GBR)   1978   2342   78,87   15,24   6,44   6000   n/a
(ex Dea Prince-08, North Prince-07, Sun Prince-89, Falderntor-89)
VOS PROSPECTOR   (GBR)   2009   1544   60,20   12,70   4,65   2011   n/a
VOS PROTECTOR   (GBR)   1983   673   46,82   11,60   6,91   2500   n/a
(ex Viking Protector-07, Cam Protector-95, Sentry Hemne-87)
VOS RAASAY   (GBR)   1983   1328   58,02   13,00   4,72   4300   n/a
(ex Viking Raasay-08, BUE Raasay-06, Norse Tide-99, Sira Supporter-96,
   Drive Supporter-85)
VOS RUNNER   (GBR)   1978/91 631   50,35   8,00   3,83   1800   n/a
(ex Dea Ranger-08, Normand Ondur-04, Balta Sound-90, Oddstein-86)
VOS SEEKER   (GBR)   2009   1544   55,20   12,70   4,65   2011   n/a
VOS SIGNAL   (BRB)   1985   1588   65,00   14,50   6,36   9180   112.0
(ex Dea Signal-08, Stirling Spica-02, Star Spica-96)
VOS SIREN   (BRB)   1982/06 686   55,00   12,19   3,66   2500   30.0
(ex Dea Siren-09, Cole Tide-05)
VOS SOUND   (VCT)   1983   1521   67,68   14,33   5,98   9280   115.0
(ex Dea Sound-09, Smit-Lloyd Sound-02, TS-52 Sound-93)
VOS SUPPLIER   (IOM)   1975   1174   5895   12,60   4,12   6160   70.0
(ex Dea Supplier-08, Normand Skipper-04)
VOS SUPPORTER   (GBR)   1983   680   46,72   11,02   6,91   2330   n/a
(ex Cam Supporter-95, Sentinel Teresa-89)
VOS SURVEYOR   (SGP)   1981   1306   55,91   12,21   4,61   3750   n/a
(ex Dea Surveyor-09, Ocean Service-07, Bigorange XVII-90)
VOS TIREE   (GBR)   1981   801   55,40   11,60   3,97   2480   n/a
(ex Viking Tiree-07, BUE Tiree-05, Supreme-99, Hornbeck Supreme-96,
   Seaboard Supreme-95, Sapucaia-90)
VOS VEDETTE   (GBR)   1970   628   46,51   9,02   4,53   1500   n/a
(ex Viking Vedette-09, Cam Vedette-95, Gnupur-92, Asthor-88, Lofottral III-81)
VOS VICTORY   (GBR)   1994   1280   55,00   12,70   4,50   1920   63.0
(ex Trafalgar Guardian-06)
VOS VIPER   (GBR)   1966   651   50,35   9,17   4,27   1560   n/a
(ex Viking Viper-07, Cam Viper-95, Hallarklettur-92, Hadja-74)
VOS VOYAGER   (GBR)   2009   1544   55,20   12,70   4,65   2011   n/a
VOS WARRIOR   (GBR)   1973   430   39,80   8,86   4,20   2000   n/a
(ex Britannia Warrior-09, Suffolk Warrior-90)
Offshore services in the North Sea
All vessels to be renamed with VOS prefix

The VOS PATHFINDER arrives at Great Yarmouth from Aberdeen on 11 June 2008 prior to carrying out stand-by duties in the southern sector of the North Sea.

(Ashley Hunn)

The SBS TYPHOON arrives at Aberdeen on 14 December 2006.

(David Dodds)

TUGS - UK

A&P FALMOUTH

The Docks, Falmouth, Cornwall, TR11 4NR
Tel : 01326 212100   Fax : 01326 319433
E-mail : falmouth@ap-group.co.uk
Website : www.ap-group.co.uk
Livery - Orange hull with white housing, black funnel with white band

ANKORVA (GBR)	1967	167	28,22	8,03	2,43	1580	20.0
(ex Komet-01, Comet-93)							
PERCUIL (GBR)	1967	167	28,22	8,03	2,43	1580	20.0
(ex Kiklop-01, Cyclop-93)							
ST PIRAN (GBR)	1979	223	29,47	8,94	2,91	2190	23.0
(ex Hallgarth-08)							

Harbour towage at Falmouth

Falmouth Bay is the setting for this view of the ANKORVA on 7 September 2008.

(David Fletcher)

ABERDEENSHIRE COUNCIL

Transportation & Infrastructure, Cape Town, Seafield Street, Banff, AB45 1ED
Tel : 01261 813483   Fax : 01261 812072
E-mail : george.cameron@@aberdeenshire.gov.uk
Websute : www.aberdeenshire.gov.uk
Livery - Blue hull with white wheelhouse

SEA HELPER (GBR)	2005		8,85	3,70	1,50	103	1.4

Towage and pilotage services at Macduff and surrounding area

ACASTER'S WATER TRANSPORT

Yokefleet Farm, Swinefleet Common, Goole, DN14 8DR
Tel/Fax : 01405 704522
E-mail : lacaster@btconnect.com

LITTLE KIRBY	(GBR)	1959		9,91	4,80	1,68	335
LITTLE SHIFTA	(GBR)	1953	18	12,50	3,73	1,75	391
(ex Snatchette-83)							
LITTLE SHUVA	(GBR)	1994	25	9,91	4,57	1,75	391

Towage services around Goole

The LITTLE SHUVA lives up to her name as she assists the KINDRED into Ocean Lock at Goole as the coaster prepares to depart on 17 April 2003.

(Malcolm Slater)

A P G MARINE

657 Prince Ave, Westcliff-On-Sea, Essex, SS0 0JB
Tel : 07941 985450
Livery - Black hull with blue housing and white wheelhouse

HORTON	(GBR)	1968	31	17,10	4,70	2,00	243	6.2
(ex DA McCann-86, Horton-79)								

Marine services on the River Thames

ASSOCIATED BRITISH PORTS

150 Holborn, London, EC1N 2LR
Tel : 020 7430 1177   Fax : 020 7430 1384

E-mail : pr@abports.co.uk
Website : www.abports.co.uk
FURNESS ABBEY   (GBR) 1997   120   19,65   6,04   1,87   720   10.6
Towage and marine services at ABP owned ports

ATLAS MARINE CONTRACTORS LTD
Harbour Entrance Lock, Imperial Dock Road, Leith Docks, Edinburgh, EH6 7DR
Tel : 0131 555 6030   Fax : 0131 555 6040
E-mail : jfrew@atlasmarine.co.uk
Website : www.atlasmarine.co.uk
KINGSTON LACY   (GBR) 1960   75   21,00   6,02   2,44   500   7.0
(ex Kingston Buci-84)
HERMES   (GBR)   1957   110   24,50   6,90   3,60   1000   10.0
Marine civil engineering services around the UK

The KINGSTON LACY is seen off Cowes on 13 July 2008

(Laurie Rufus)

G BAKER MARINE LTD
Eastern Docks, Ocean Gate, Atlantic Way, Southampton, SO14 3QN
Tel : 023 8033 7889   Fax : 023 8023 0041
E-mail : gbakemarine@tiscali.co.uk
CHIEF   (GBR)   1930   72   720   10.0
(ex Chiefton-08, Chief-04, Filip)
DEBORAH   (GBR)   1958   35   16,76   4,05   2,30   143
(ex M.S.C. Deborah-88)

DIDO (GBR)	1958	35	16,76	4,05	2,30	140	

(ex M.S.C. Dido-88)

JOAN (GBR)	1972	50	18,28	5,26	2,59	330	3.3
SUSAN (GBR)	1968	80	21,50	6,40	2,90	600	6.0

(ex Wyepress, Felicity-98)

Towage around south coast of England

BAKER TRAYTE MARINE LTD
1 Grand Division Row, Henderson Road, Southsea, Hampshire, PO4 9GD
Tel : 023 9229 4800   Fax : 023 9272 6953
E-mail : info@btmarine.co.uk
Website : www.btmarine.co.uk
Livery - Black hull with dark yellow wheelhouse

AGWI (GBR)	1979		10,00	3,80	1,50	200	2.5
PAUL H (GBR)	1991		14,00	5,00	1,50	360	3.5
PRENTICE (GBR)	1980		12,00	3,60	1,50	120	1.2
VOE III (GBR)			14,00	6,00	2,00	424	

Marine services around Portsmouth and south coast

BARTLETT CREEK SHIPPING LTD (ALAN PRATT)
139 Watling Street, Gillingham, Kent, ME7 2YY
Tel : 01634 234147
Livery - Various

CHRISTINE (GBR)	1966	77	22,10	6,25	2,50	495	6.0
NIPASHORE (GBR)	1983	18	13,20	4,00	1,75	180	1.5

Also operates the small tugs BOA and CLOUD

Towage services on the River Thames

BAY TOWAGE & SALVAGE CO LTD
Anchorline Basin, Ramsden Dock, Barrow-in-Furness, Cumbria, LA14 2TB
Tel : 01229 830388   Fax : 01229 871011
E-mail : info@baytowage.co.uk
Website : www.baytowage.co.uk
Livery - Black hull, white wheelhouse with dayglow orange band on top

ALBICORE (GBR)	1990	110	19,80	6,70	2,40	800	8.0
(ex Sarah C-01)							
AVANTI C (GBR)	1978	33	15,25	4,75	1,80	480	5.0
KAMSAR (GBR)	1982	40	15,70	4,80	2,20	730	7.6
TIOGA B (GBR)	1988	38	15,93	5,30	2,20	730	11.0

(ex Anglian Maid-95, Gray Delta-91)

Towage services at Barrow-in-Furness and coastal contracting

BENNETT'S BARGES

Isle of Grain, Rochester, Kent, ME3 OAG
Tel : 01634 272208   Fax : 01634 271197
E-mail : david.allen@aggregate.com
Website : www.bennetts-tugs.co.uk
Livery - Black hull with white trim, white housing and blue funnel, black top separated by white band.

ARGONAUT (GBR)	1963	115	26,00	7,00	3,60	875	13.0
SEA CHALLENGE II (GBR)	1969	70	20,36	6,70	2,94	1060	13.0
(ex Eduard-00, Jumbo-83, Argus 5)							
STEVEN B (GBR)	1971	58	25,24	5,50	2,50	1200	15.0
(ex Bever-00)							

Also operate a fleet of barges and lighters

Towage and lighterage services on the River Thames and River Medway

A company within Aggregate Industries UK Ltd

The ARGONAUT and SEA CHALLENGE II, then in Foster Yeoman colours, are seen at Strood on 11 June 2006.

(Bernard McCall)

THE BIG DITCH SHIPPING CO LTD

Dry Docks House, Manchester Dry Docks, Trafford Wharf Road, Trafford Park, Manchester, M17 1HA
Tel : 0161 873 8818   Fax : 0161 873 8819

CLIFTON (GBR)	1974		12,70	3,70	1,80	360	5.0

Towage and barge services on the Manchester Ship Canal

B. K. MARINE LTD
Veensgarth, Tingwall, Shetland, ZE2 9SB
Tel : 01595 840208   Fax : 01595 840630
E-mail : boats@herrisleahouse.co.uk
Website : www.bkmarine.co.uk
Livery - Black hull with cream wheelhouse
BAGHEERA   (GBR)   1990   17,40   7,50   2,00   500   6.5
Also workboat KOADA
Marine services UK and northern Europe

PORT OF BLYTH
South Harbour, Blyth, Northumberland, NE24 3PB
Tel : 01670 352066   Fax : 01670 355169
E-mail : enquiries@blythport.co.uk
Website : www.portofblyth.co.uk
Livery - Light blue hull and white wheelhouse with orange trim
BLYTH
     ENDEAVOUR   (GBR) 1991   43   16,89   5,29   2,10   600   6.0
Bed levelling and harbour towage on east coast of England

BOATWERK (THAMES) LTD
British Gypsum Jetty, Church Manorway, Erith, Kent, DA8 1BQ
Tel : 01322 438305
Livery - Red hull, white wheelhouse with red band round the top
MONARCH M   (GBR)   2000   9,80   3,00   1,40   180   1.2
Also operate a fleet of small open workboats
Towage and marine services on the River Thames

PORT OF BOSTON
Boston, Lincolnshire, PE21 6BN
Tel : 01205 365571   Fax : 01205 310126
E-mail : info@portofboston.co.uk
Website : www.portofboston.co.uk
Livery - Black hull, white housing and wheelhouse with buff funnel
BOSTONIAN   (GBR)   1967   50   21,30   6,10   2,00   528   7.0
Towage services at port of Boston

BP NORSE MARINE (UK)
Cleverley Cottage, Dean Lane, Dean, Bishop's Waltham, Southampton, SO32 1FX
Mobile Tel : 07974 178146   Tel/Fax : 01489 890031
E-mail : jan@bpnorsemarine.co.uk
Website : www.bpnorsemarine.co.uk

STOREBROR* (GBR) 1946 54 19,83 5,60 2,40 825 12.0
(ex Karnfjord-64, Cement 7-58, TID 180-46)
* The name of this tug is also written as STORBROR
Towage, dredging and marine services around south of England

BRIGGS MARINE
Seaforth House, Seaforth Place, Burntisland, Fife, KY3 9AX
Tel : 01592 872939   Fax : 01592 873975
E-mail : marketing@briggsmarine.com
Website : www.briggsmarine.com
Livery - Black hull, white housing and wheelhouse with buff funnel

FORTH JOUSTER	(GBR)	2008	255	26,00	11,50	2,25	2400	33.1
FORTH BOXER	(GBR)	1995	83	18,60	6,06	1,65	440	6.0
FORTH CONSTRUCTOR								
	(GBR)	1967/94	265	28,50	9,45	2,58	1240	17.5
(ex Broodbank-95)								
FORTH								
DRUMMER	(GBR)	1967	114	25,30	7,00	2,60	1364	16.0
(ex Lady Laura-00)								
FORTH FIGHTER	(GBR)	1985/01	55	23,50	7,50	1,50	640	8.0
(ex Gemsar-01)								
FORTH HUNTER	(SGP)	2008	467	37,00	11,40	4,05	2700	35.0
FORTH SENTINEL	(GBR)	1991	235	28,25	9,69	2,50	1080	n/a
(ex Humber Sentinel-08)								
JOSINE	(GBR)	1974		13,00	3,40	2,00	240	
SYLVESTER	(GBR)	1974		14,00	6,00	0,90	320	

Coastal towage and marine civil engineering

BRISTOL CITY COUNCIL
Harbour Office, Underfall Yard, Cumberland Road, Bristol, BS1 6XG
Tel : 0117 903 1484   Fax : 0117 903 1487
E-mail : harbour.office@bristol.gov.uk
Website : www.bristol.gov.uk/bristolharbour

BRISTOLIAN	(GBR)	1979		15,12	4,68	2,10	565	5.4
(ex Herman Jr-08, En Avant 9-03, Zal 4-80)							

Towage and escort services on the River Avon

BRISTOL INDUSTRIAL MUSEUM
Princes Wharf, Wapping Road, Bristol, BS1 4RN
Tel : 0117 925 1470

JOHN KING	(GBR)	1935	49	19,81	5,18	2,16	300	n/a
(ex Durdham-92, Pride-86, Peter Leigh-78)								
MAYFLOWER	(GBR)	1861	32	19,29	3,65	2,19	150	n/a

Two preserved tugs in the City Docks, Bristol

JAMES BUTCHER & SONS LTD
14 Broad Street, Portsmouth, Hants, PO1 2JE
Tel : 023 9282 2584   Fax : 023 9287 4666
E-mail : tug@blueboattrips.com
Livery - Sky blue hull with white wheelhouse and company emblem

CAROL JAMES	(GBR)	1983	40	15,30	4,60	2,20	385	5.0
GARY JAMES	(GBR)	1985		14,45	4,40	2,00	360	5.0
(ex Breevaer 17-91)								
GUY JAMES	(GBR)	1995	57	16,90	5,29	2,10	940	13.5
JACK JAMES	(GBR)	2002	57	16,90	5,29	2,30	1080	14.0
JANET JAMES	(GBR)	1983		14,20	4,20	2,00	480	3.8

Also operate small pleasure craft

Towage services at Portsmouth

The JANET JAMES makes a fine sight as she leaves Portsmouth harbour on 16 July 2006

(Chris Jones)

C & R DIVING LTD
Unit 19, Sellaness Industrial Estate, Graven, Mossbank, Shetland, ZE2 9UR
Tel : 01806 242755   Fax : 01806 242750
E-mail : candrdiving1@aol.com
Website : www.candrdiving.co.uk

HEGRIE	(GBR)	1988	30	12,49	6,70	0,91	360
(ex Zeepaard)							

Marine services around the Shetland Islands

CAERNARFON HARBOUR TRUST
Harbour Office, Slate Quay, Caernarfon, Gwynedd, LL55 2PB
Tel : 01286 672118   Fax : 01286 678729
E-mail : cht@caernarfon-hbr.demon.co.uk
Website : www.caernarfonharbour.co.uk
Livery - Dark blue hull with white wheelhouse

SEIONT IV (GBR)	2007		12,80	6,20	1,70	338	3.1

Marine services in the Menai Straits

CARDIFF COMMERCIAL BOAT OPERATORS LTD
24 Clive Street, Cardiff, CF11 7JB
Mobile Tel : 07850 861649
Livery - Black hull with white wheelhouse

NEW ROSS 1 (GBR)	1986	20	14,40	4,20	2,05	349	7.5

Towage and marine services in South Wales and the Bristol Channel

The NEW ROSS 1 tows the former Fowey tug CANNIS, now substantially altered, down the River Avon on 20 September 2008.

(Bernard McCal.

NODDY CARDY
21 Navik Close, Maldon, CM9 6UX
Tel : 01621 853458

AGAMA (GBR)	1969	77	22,30	6,25	2,50	660	6.0
(ex Dorothy-91)							
GW 108 (GBR)	1966	17	18,25	4,50		400	4.0

Towage services at the port of Brightlingsea and on the Norfolk Broads

CARMET TUG COMPANY LTD

44 Private Drive, Barnston, Wirral, CH61 1DE
Tel : 0151 327 8018   Fax : 0151 328 1212
E-mail : tugs@carmet.co.uk
Website : www.carmet.co.uk
Livery - Black hull with white wheelhouse and cream housing

AUDREY (GBR)	1961	57	18,74	5,18	2,29	495	6.5
(ex Stint-00, Cherry-85, Audrey-84)							
M.S.C. VICEROY (GBR)	1973	137	28,38	7,81	3,44	1280	14.0
M.S.C. VICTORY (GBR)	1973	137	28,38	7,81	3,44	1280	14.0
M.S.C. VIKING (GBR)	1973	137	28,38	7,81	3,44	1280	14.0
M.S.C. VOLANT (GBR)	1973	137	28,38	7,31	3,44	1280	14.0
VIGOUR (GBR)	1966	33	15,40	5,50	1,90	375	n/a
(ex Pushdale H, Baas)							

Coastal towage and towage services on the Manchester Ship Canal

In customary immaculate condition, the MSC VOLANT passes Ellesmere Port on 24 September 2006.

(Alan Faulkner)

CATTEWATER HARBOUR COMMISSIONERS

2 The Barbican, Plymouth, Devon, PL1 2LR
Tel : 01752 665934   Fax : 01752 253624
E-mail : info@plymouthport.org.uk
Website : www.plymouthport.org
Livery - Blue hull with white wheelhouse

PRINCE ROCK (GBR)	2003	100	18,87	6,56	2,50	1400	17.5

Towage services at Plymouth

ROB CHANDLER
22 Harvesters Close, Rainham, Kent, ME8 8PA
Tel : 01634 389175

TOUCHSTONE	(GBR)	1962	69	22,46	5,84		528	

Preserved in private ownership and operational

CLYDE MARINE SERVICES LTD
Victoria Harbour, Greenock, PA15 1HW
Tel : 01475 721281   Fax : 01475 888023
E-mail : enquiries@clyde-marine.co.uk
Website : www.clyde-marine.co.uk
Livery - Navy blue hull with buff wheelhouse

BATTLER	(GBR)	2004	110	19,65	6,04	2,70	1440	20.8
BEAVER BAY	(GBR)	1977	42	16,00	4,80	1,80	380	5.0
(ex Loch Shiel)								
BITER	(GBR)	1982	42	16,00	4,80	1,30	796	11.0
(ex Haki-01, Salud-82)								
BOOJUM BAY	(GBR)	1964	30	15,73	4,50	2,22	365	5.0
(ex Medway-91, Niger-64)								
BRUISER	(GBR)	2007	50	19,33	7,33	2,92	2000	28.0

Also operate small pleasure craft; tendering and boatman services

Towage services on the River Clyde

CLYDEPORT OPERATIONS LTD
Greenock Ocean Terminal, Patrick Street, Greenock, PA16 8UU
Tel : 01475 726171   Fax : 01475 888130
Website : www.clydeport.co.uk
Livery - Navy blue hull with white wheelhouse

TORCH	(GBR)	1993	135	20,00	9,00	1,50	760	8.0
(ex Marineco Seeonee-06, MCS Nikki-04, Diana-96)								

Marine services on the River Clyde

COASTAL LAUNCH SERVICES LTD
The Saeter, East Boldre, Nr. Brockenhurst, Hampshire, SO42 7WU
Tel : 01590 626247 / 01590 626287   Fax : 01590 626301
E-mail : coastallaunch@btconnect.com
Website : www.coastallaunchservicesltd.co.uk
Livery - Various

JESSICA S	(GBR)	1983	126	20,02	9,15	1,50	925	9.5
(ex S.B.1 -92)								
SARAH GREY	(GBR)	1999	107	25,00	9,60	1,85	1400	18.0

Marine civil engineering and dredging support

The SARAH GREY was photographed at Pembroke Dock on 2 October 2006.

(Dominic McCall)

COASTLINE SURVEYS LTD

Pearces Mill, Falmouth Wharf, North Parade, Falmouth, Cornwall, TR11 2TF
Tel : 01326 311220　　Fax : 01326 314262　　Mob : 07802 786757
E-mail : info@coastlinesurveys.co.uk
Website : www.coastlinesurveys.co.uk
Livery - Blue hull with white housing and blue funnel

FLAT HOLM	(GBR)	1976	129	24,00	7,42	2,89	700	10.0

(ex UKD Flat Holm-99, Flat Holm-97, Al Khubar 3-86)
Marine civil engineering and survey services

COASTWORKS

Coastworks Operations Ltd, 8 Allanton Park Terrace, Fairlie, Ayrshire, KA29 0AW
Tel : 01475 568572　　Fax : 01475 568153
E-mail : info@coastworks.co.uk
Website : www.coastworks.co.uk

BEN CROM	(GBR)	1966/08	70	21,00	6,40	1,75	400	3.5
CHALLENGER								
OF LEITH	(GBR)	2007	32	15,00	6,60	1,36	570	6.0
REGIS 2	(GBR)	1977/02		10,60	3,60	1,10	160	1.6

Also operate small workboats and survey boats
Workboats, tugs and barge suppliers to the marine industry throughout the UK and Europe

Princes Dock, Glasgow, is the setting for this view of the REGIS 2 on 8 August 2008. The name of this vessel is also given as REGIS II in some sources.

(Dominic McCall)

COLERAINE HARBOUR COMMISSIONERS

Harbour Office, 4 Riversdale Road, Coleraine, BT52 1RY
Tel : 028 7034 2012   Fax : 028 7035 2000
E-mail : coleraineharbour@aol.com
Livery - Dark blue hull with white wheelhouse

CONFIDENCE	(GBR)	1983	38	16,80	5,20	2,50	720	11.0

(ex Plym Echo-04, Gray Echo-96)
Marine services at the port of Coleraine

CONOCO LTD

Tetney Oil Terminal, Tetney Lock Road, Grimsby, DN36 5NX
Tel : 01472 814101

MONOGIRL	(GBR)	1972	30	15,75	4,88	1,99	360	n/a
MONOGIRL 2	(GBR)	2008	48	16,50	5,45	2,54	322	6.0

Marine services assisting shuttle tankers off Tetney monobuoy on the River Humber

CORY ENVIRONMENTAL LTD

Riverside, Charlton, London, SE7 7SU
Tel : 0208 853 5434   Fax : 0208 858 8388
E-mail : info@coryenvironmental.co.uk
Website : www.coryenvironmental.co.uk
Livery - Black hull with white housing and black/white/black funnel with company logo

GENERAL VIII (GBR)	1965	77	25,69	6,40	3,14	1196	11.0
MERIT (GBR)	1964	83	25,30	6,40	2,74	1196	11.0
(ex Lingo)							
MERSINA (GBR)	1955	79	24,38	5,97	2,74	750	10.0
(ex Repulse-57)							
RECRUIT (GBR)	1952	91	24,38	5,97	2,93	1196	11.0
REGAIN (GBR)	1998	113	26,50	9,40	2,30	1610	17.5
RESOLVE (GBR)	1994	42	15,24	4,87	1,10	250	3.0
RETAINER (GBR)	1979	120	23,55	6,60	2,50	2096	13.4
(ex Oil Retainer-90)							

Also operate a fleet of barges
Lighterage and waste disposal services on the River Thames

The REGAIN in the River Thames on 19 October 2008.

(Steve Cracknell)

CUMBRIA COUNTY COUNCIL (PORT OF WORKINGTON)
Harbour Office, Prince of Wales Dock, Workington, Cumbria, CA14 2JH
Tel : 01900 602301   Fax : 01900 604696
E-mail : workington.port@cumbriacc.gov.uk
Website : www.portofworkington.co.uk
Livery - Black hull with blue bulwarks and white wheelhouse with orange trim wheelhouse

DERWENT (GBR)	1992	120	16,89	5,29	2,00	722	10.5

Towage and pilot launch services at Workington

D J CUNNINGHAM

20 Greencastle Pier Road, Kilkeel, Newry, County Down, BT34 4LR
Tel : 02841 769401
Livery - Black hull, brown housing and white wheelhouse with buff funnel

MOURNE SHORE	(GBR)	1964	101	22,99	7,45	2,59	800	14.0
(ex Bugsier 29-93)								
MOURNE VALLEY	(GBR)	1961	57	18,6	5,30	2,70	495	7.0
(ex Afon Cefni-89, Alice)								

Towage services in the Carlingford Lough area

This view of the MOURNE SHORE in Carlingford Lough on 13 September 2007 clearly reveals her origin as a former Bugsier tug.

(David McNamee)

DANIEL ADAMSON PRESERVATION SOCIETY

Website : www.danieladamson.com

DANIEL ADAMSON	(GBR)	1903	173	33,53	7,47	2,64	250	n/a
(ex Ralph Brocklebank-36)								

Undergoing restoration on Merseyside

DEANS TUGS & WORKBOATS LTD

63 Harbour Way, Hull, HU9 1PL
Tel : 01482 219277
Livery - Black and blue hull, blue housing and white wheelhouse with blue funnel and white stripe

FELIX TOW	(GBR)	1955	28	15,00	4,20	2,50	250	2.5
(ex Felix-Tow)								

FREIGHT
| ENDEAVOUR (GBR) | 1967/74 | 38 | 18,00 | 4,88 | 2,50 | 420 | 3.0 |

(ex Placer-74)

GILLIAN KNIGHT (GBR)	1956	32	18,75	4,88	2,13	250	2.0
LASHETTE (GBR)	1971	156	24,00	8,50	2,60	730	10.0
LINFORD (GBR)	1966	122	26,70	7,80	4,00	1600	16.0

(ex Plankton-91)

MARY (GBR)	1973	50	18,28	5,26	2,59	330	3.3
DORSETT (GBR)	1966	122	26,70	7,80	4,00	1600	16.0

(ex Placard-91)

PRIMROSE (GBR)	1906	53	22,60	4,90	2,70	540	5.4
SHOVETTE (GBR)	1974	156	24,00	8,50	2,60	720	10.0

(ex Grey Lash-83)

SPEEDWELL (GBR)	1967	50	17,07	4,88	2,44	330	2.5

Towage services at Hull and the River Humber

DELTA MARINE
5 Gladstone Terrace, Lerwick, Shetland, ZE1 0EG
Tel : 01595 694799   Fax : 01595 692685
E-mail : delta.marine@zetnet.co.uk
Website : www.delta-marine.co.uk
Livery - Blue hull with white housing and company emblem

VOE JARL (GBR)	2007	161	26,00	11,50	2,25	2400	33.0
VOE SERVICE (GBR)	1989	55	18,42	6,00	1,70	480	7.5
VOE VENTURE (GBR)	1994	71	22,42	8,04	2,00	1000	13.5
VOE VIKING (GBR)	2007	161	26,00	11,50	2,25	2400	33.0

Towage, anchor handling and marine civil engineering services around Europe

DIVEMEX LTD
Station Yard, Caersws Powys, SY17 5HH
Tel : 01686 688505   Fax : 01686 688383

OLIVER (VCT)	1975	326	38,16	9,66	3,81	2679	38.0

(ex Boquhan-97)

Marine services in Africa

DOVER HARBOUR BOARD
Harbour House, Marine Parade, Dover, Kent, CT17 9BU
Tel : 01304 240400   Fax : 01304 240465
Website : www.doverport.co.uk
Livery - Dark blue hull with white housing and blue funnel

DHB DAUNTLESS (GBR)	2000	304	30,82	10,20	4,08	4820	55.0
DHB DOUGHTY (GBR)	2000	304	30,82	10,20	4,08	4820	55.0

Harbour towage services at the port of Dover

The VOE JARL leaves Workington on a sunny 15 November 2008. She is heading for a wind farm under construction off the Cumbrian coast.

(Derek McAlone)

The DHB DAUNTLESS off her home port on 23 October 2006.

(Dominic McCall)

DUNBERRY MARINE LTD
Ibrox, Ollaberry, Shetland, ZE2 9RT
Tel : 0560 262 7650
E-mail : info@dunberry marine.com
Website : www.dunberrymarine.com
NORTHERN
 FALCON   (GBR)   2008   21,60   9,04   3,0   1200   14.0

DUNKIRK LITTLE SHIPS RESTORATION TRUST
The Cottage By The Lake, Chilling Lane, Warsash, Southampton, SO31 9HF
Tel : 01489 572775
E-mail : jerry.lewis@care4free.net
Website : www.dlsrt.org.uk
CHALLENGE   (GBR)   1931   238   30,47   8,01   1,98   1100   n/a
Preserved tug seen at various ports on the south coast of England

The CHALLENGE in steam at Southampton on 7 June 2003.

(Bernard McCall)

EEL PIE ISLAND SLIPWAYS LTD
Eel Pie Island, Twickenham, TW1 3DY
Tel : 020 8891 4481   Fax : 020 8892 5590
DANCHA   (GBR)   1961   14   12,95   3,35   1,92   110
(ex Smudge-02, Dancha)
Towage services around Eel Pie Island on the River Thames

ENVIRONMENT AGENCY

Kings Meadow House, Kings Meadow Road, Reading, Berkshire, RG1 8DQ
Tel : 0118 953 5533   Fax : 0118 959 2160
E-mail : enquiries@environment-agency.gov.uk
Website : www.environment-agency.gov.uk
Livery - Black hull, green housing and white wheelhouse with buff funnel

FALCONBROOK (GBR)	1958	22	13,72	4,18	1,70	260	
(ex Caspar C-02, General V-84, Blackboys-76)							
VER (GBR)	1956	14	13,41	3,20	1,37	178	1.5
(ex Brent Lee)							

Emergency towing services on the upper Thames

FELIXARC MARINE LTD

North Quay, The Dock, Felixstowe, IP11 8SY
Tel : 01394 676497   Fax : 01394 674039
Website : www.felixarcmarine.co.uk
Livery - Black hull with white housing, black funnel with yellow band

GRAY MAMMOTH (GBR)	1989	224	27,05	10,00	2,06	804	14.0
GRAY SALVOR (GBR)	1991	40	16,50	5,20	2,58	850	11.0
GRAY TEST (GBR)	1996	55	19,50	6,04	2,60	1342	17.5
(ex Anglian Man-00)							
GRAY VIXEN (GBR)	1991	40	16,50	5,20	2,58	850	11.0
HT BLADE (GBR)	1990	371	30,64	10,24	4,11	3860	43.0
(ex Adsteam Deben-07, Deben-07)							

Coastal towage and marine civil engineering, harbour towage at Great Yarmouth
Part of the A P Møller - Mærsk Group

The GRAY TEST at speed in Great Yarmouth Roads on 1 April 2008.

(Dominic McCall)

FENDERCARE LTD

Enterprise House, Harveys Lane, Seething, Norfolk, NR15 1EN
Tel : 01508 482666   Fax : 01508 482710

CHARLES PLANE	(GBR)	1965	152	28,96	7,60	3,66	920	15.0

(ex Lowgarth-06)
Towage of fenders in Nigeria

FENLAND DISTRICT COUNCIL

Harbour Master's Office, West Bank, Sutton Bridge, Lincolnshire, PE12 9QR
Tel : 01406 351530   Fax : 01406 351350
Livery - Black with white wheelhouse

FENLANDER	(GBR)	1999	35	14,44	4,73	2,05	600	7.6

Towage and pilot launch services at Sutton Bridge and other Wash ports

The *FENLANDER* had assisted a coaster in the River Nene when photographed at Wisbech on 7 July 2008.

(Bernard McCall)

DAVID FERRAN & SONS

2nd Floor, Hurst House, 15/19 Corporation Square, Belfast, BT1 3AJ
Tel : 028 9032 5751   Fax : 028 9043 8470
E-mail : justin@davidferran.co.uk
Website : www.davidferran.co.uk
Livery - Dark blue hull with white trim and white housing

EILEEN	(GBR)	1975		9,14	4,17	2,00	127	2.0
FARSET								
OF BELFAST	(GBR)	2003		15,40	5,20	1,80	1100	14.6
LB1	(GBR)	2008		8,50	3,41	1,20	125	

SALLY (GBR)	1975		9,14	4,17	2,00	127	2.0
VERA LOCKHART (GBR)	1974		10,47	4,27	2,00	250	3.5

Light towage and line-handling in Belfast

FORTH ESTUARY TOWAGE LTD
1 Prince of Wales Dock, Edinburgh, EH6 7DX
Tel : 0131 555 8700   Fax : 0131 553 7462
Website : www.forthports.co.uk
Livery - Black hull with cream housing, blue funnel with company badge

BEAMER (GBR)	1983	251	29,42	8,42	2,65	1800	20.0
FIDRA (GBR)	1995	363	30,00	11,50	4,30	5400	52.0
OXCAR (GBR)	1978	250	30,64	9,33	2,71	2660	30.0
SEAL CARR (GBR)	1983	251	29,42	8,92	3,06	1800	20.0

Harbour towage at Leith and in the Firth of Forth

FOWEY HARBOUR COMMISSIONERS
Harbour Office, Albert Quay, Fowey, Cornwall, PL23 1AJ
Tel : 01726 832471/2   Fax : 01726 833738
E-mail : fhc@foweyharbour.co.uk
Website : www.foweyharbour.co.uk
Livery - Black and green hull with yellow trim, buff and cream housing and wheelhouse

MORGAWR (GBR)	1980	223	28,45	8,50	4,50	2190	23.5
(ex Holmgarth-08)							
PENLEATH (GBR)	1980	n/a	12,72	4,20	1,66	360	3.2
(ex DTS Seal-88, Yarra-87)							
TREGEAGLE (GBR)	1964	131	28,20	7,19	3,36	1000	15.0
(ex Forth-86, Flying Demon-84)							

Harbour towage and marine services at Fowey and other ports in Devon and Cornwall

GARELOCH SUPPORT SERVICES (PLANT) LTD
Rhu Marina, Rhu, Argyll & Bute, G84 8LH
Tel : 01436 821277   Fax : 01436 821288
E-mail : info@gssplant.co.uk
Website : www.gssplant.co.uk
Livery - Black hull, white housing, dark blue funnel

JULIA M (GBR)	1975		10,00	5,00	1,80	180	2.0
LAURA M (GBR)	2002	68	20,20	8,25	1,85	525	12.0
LESLEY M (GBR)	1994	135	20,00	9,00	1,50	760	8.0
(ex MCS Menno-04, Sabrina-96)							
MAGGIE M (GBR)	2008		22,00	9,00	1,80	1600	20.0
MARY M (GBR)	1999	44	15,82	7,42	1,50	504	5.0
MEGAN M (GBR)	1965/07		24,00	8,50	2,25	1600	19.5
(ex Stoneness-06, MCL1-05, Eness-02, Stoneness-00)							
MORAG M (GBR)	2008		21,60	9,04	3,00	1600	20.0

Marine civil engineering around the UK

Multipurpose vessels such as the LESLEY M differ radically from conventional tugs.
(Danny Kelliher Jr.)

GENERAL MARINE TUGS & BARGES LTD

54 Orchard Place, London, E14 0JW
Tel : 020 7265 1854   Fax : 020 7702 2766
Livery - Black hull, red housing and white wheelhouse, white funnel with red diamond
LORD

DEVONPORT	(GBR)	1959	109	25,73	6,76	3,04	935	
REGARDER	(GBR)	1958	69	22,43	5,70	2,71	500	6.0
(ex Regard-91)								
REVENGE	(GBR)	1948	61	21,34	5,36	2,54	500	7.0
SIR AUBREY	(GBR)	1962	59	22,25	5,18	2,89	457	9.0
(ex Margaret Barry-88, Sir Aubrey)								
SUNCREST	(GBR)	1961	144	28,58	7,45	3,37	1340	13.0
(ex Sunwind-85, Sun XXIII-84)								
TILLY	(GBR)	1955	25	15,48	4,80	1,25	300	
(ex Zwerver-92, Zwerver II-88, Marker II-84)								
WAVERLEY	(GBR)	1960	109	25,73	6,76	3,04	935	
(ex Lord Waverley)								

Towage services on the River Thames

GPS MARINE CONTRACTORS LTD

Lockside House, Chatham Docks, Kent, ME4 4SW
Tel : 01634 401444   Fax : 01634 893983
E-mail : enquiries@gpsmarine.co.uk
Website : wwwgpsmarine.com
Livery - Black hull with brown housing and white wheelhouse, black funnel with white band
bearing the letters GPS

Name		Year							
ALEXANDRA	(GBR)	1963	164	30,64	8,08	3,70	1050	18.0
FRISTON DOWN	(GBR)	1964	99	24,97	6,20	3,30	1250	20.0
GPS ANGLIA	(GBR)	1982	218	33,02	10,50	4,42	3200	32.0
(ex RM Margaux-07, Rupelmonde-02)								
HAULIER	(GBR)	1938	14	13,72	3,73	1,30	220	3.0
(ex Nat 113-44, Haulier-42, Hauler-38)								
IBERIA	(NLD)	1958	18	22,90	6,25	2,35	900	
(ex Eerland 4-08, Smit Spanje-99, Kapelle-58)								
IONIA	(GBR)	1956		22,50	5,16	1,71	565	
(ex Jenny-08, Noordster 7-87, Docat 3-78, Fiat Voluntas XIX-76)								
MURIA	(GBR)	1960	128	29,21	6,94	3,00	900	16.0
(ex GP America-02, Independent II-00)								
NAPIA	(GBR)	1965	128	29,21	6,94	3,00	900	16.0
(ex Volharding 12-00)								
RACIA	(GBR)	1964	78	24,80	6,02	2,90	600	9.0
(ex Condor IX-02, Condor-00, Pieter Goedkoop-82)								
RICHARD HART	(GBR)	1951	75	19,84	4,06	2,25	400	5.3
(ex William George-75)								
VINCIA	(GBR)	1963/08	42	18,28	5,26	2,70	400	4.5
(ex Neptune)								
ZEEPIA	(NLD)	1955	18	21,32	6,02	2,71	700	10.0
(ex Zeepaard-05, Phoenix-68)								

Also operate floating sheerlegs, barges and workboats

Marine services on the River Thames, River Medway, Rotterdam and coastal towage

When seen in the River Thames on 28 October 2008, the recently-acquired IBERIA was flying a Red Ensign despite her Rotterdam registry.

(Krispen Atkinson)

GREEN BARGE COMPANY LTD

The Barge Terminal, 27-28 Berth, Tilbury Freeport, Tilbury, Essex, RM18 7HB
Tel : 01375 844631   Fax : 01375 855402
E-mail : info@greenbarge.co.uk
Website : www.greenbarge.co.uk
Livery - Black hull with white trim, lime green housing and white wheelhouse

GREEN LONDON	(GBR)	1959	109	25,73	6,76	3,04	1000	15.0

(ex Jim Higgs-08, Lord Ritchie-85)
Also operate the small tugs FALCONBROOK and NASEBY
Marine services on the River Thames

GRESHORNISH WORKBOATS

Glamaig Place, Portree, Isle of Skye, IV51 9PJ
Tel : 01478 611911   Fax : 01478 611911

PORTREE GIRL	(GBR)	1993		23,50	6,60	2,70	760	12.0

Marine services around the west coast of Scotland

GRIFFIN TOWAGE & MARINE

Organford Manor, Poole, Dorset, BH16 6ES
Mobile Tel : 07956 351933   Fax : 01202 623724
E-mail : jon@griffintowage.co.uk
Website : www.griffintowage.co.uk
Livery - Black hull with buff housing, white and buff wheelhouse with red tirm

GOLIATH	(GBR)	1956	169	29,16	7,88	3,32	1400	17.0
KINGSTON	(GBR)	1962	113	26,90	6,99	3,00	720	23.0
KNIGHTON	(GBR)	1943	80	22,37	5,74	2,60	660	10.0
PRINCETON	(GBR)	1965	148	28,70	7,60	3,90	1350	20.0

(ex M.S.C. Sceptre-86)
(ex Sun XXIV-92)
(ex Duchess-07, Red Duchess-06, Accomplice-98, GW 94-76, Phoenix-65, Ierland-57)
(ex Kapitan Engler-05, Alex Falck-03, Kapitän Engler-02)
Coastal towage around the UK coast

H & S MARINE LTD

Velvarend Hoop, The Quay, Burnham-on-Crouch, Essex, CM0 8AS
Tel/Fax : 01206 763147
E-mail : howard@handsmarineltd.com
Website : www.handsmarineltd.com
Livery - Orange hull with black trim and white wheelhouse

HERMAN SR	(GBR)	1976		15,85	4,40	2,00	500	7.0
ANETTE B	(GBR)	2008	123	23,35	8,64	2,05	1718	22.0

Towage and marine services around the English Coast

The GOLIATH breaks through the mist as she leaves Lowestoft on 18 February 2006.

(Ashley Hunn

The JANETTE B passes Gorleston as she speeds out of Great Yarmouth on 21 April 2008.

(Ashley Hunn

HARWICH HAVEN AUTHORITY
Harbour House, The Quay, Harwich, Essex, CO12 3HH
Tel : 01255 243030   Fax : 01255 241302
E-mail : harbour.house@hha.co.uk
Website : www.hha.co.uk
Livery - Blue hull with white housing and wheelhouse
HAVEN

HORNBILL	(GBR)	2002		20,20	8,24	1,40	1104	12.0

Towage, marine and pollution services at Harwich

HEYSHAM BOAT CHARTER LTD
1 Basil Grove, Overton, Morecambe, Lancs, LA3 3JD
Tel : 01524 858354   Fax : 01524 859885
E-mail : seatrojan@aol.com
Website : www.hbc.uk.com
Livery - Black hull and white housing

SEA TROJAN	(GBR)	1963	117	24,41	7,35	3,00	850	14.5

Coastal towage around the UK and support of marine civil engineering

The SEA TROJAN was one of the many tugs and workboats used to support engineering work during the construction of two terminals for the import of liquefied natural gas on Milford Haven. Our photograph was taken on 16 September 2005.

(Chris Jones)

HOLYHEAD TOWING COMPANY LTD

Newry Beach Yard, Holyhead, Anglesey, LL65 1YB
Tel : 01407 760111   Fax : 01407 764531
E-mail : towing@holyhead.co.uk
Website : www.holyhead.co.uk
Livery - Black hull with white housing, red funnel with company badge

AFON BRAINT	(CYP)	2005	200	25,50	9,00	2,40	2600	34.0
AFON CADNANT	(CYP)	2007	477	35,00	11,50	2,40	5100	54.0
AFON CARADOG	(GBR)	2006	200	26,80	9,00	2,40	2600	34.0
AFON CEFNI	(GBR)	2002	101	22,50	7,50	2,00	1280	17.0
AFON GOCH	(GBR)	1997	129	23,80	7,50	2,00	1450	19.0
AFON LLIGWY	(GBR)	2002	119	22,35	8,60	2,00	1460	19.1
(ex Herman-05)								
AFON WEN	(GBR)	1984	60	19,55	6,60	2,40	1040	15.0
(ex Wyeguard-00, Antje-97)								
LLANDDWYN								
ISLAND	(GBR)	1994	114	21,50	7,80	2,00	940	14.0
NORTH STACK	(GBR)	1984	15	13,30	4,80	1,50	430	6.0
(ex Kinnel-03, Kinghow-02)								
PUFFIN ISLAND	(GBR)	2003	167	26,00	11,50	1,75	2300	30.0
(ex Zwerver II-08)								

*The construction of a new outer harbour at Great Yarmouth is another major marine civ,
engineering enterprise which has required the use of various tugs to support construction or t*
*tow barges bringing materials for use on the site. Holyhead Towing's AFON WEN returns fror,
the construction site on 4 August 2007.*

(Ashley Hunn

Managed by Caspiisky Buksir (Kazakhstan)

AK BURKUT (KAZ)	2008	477	35,00	11,50	2,40	3400	54.5
(ex Afon Cymryan-08)							
AK SUNKAR (KAZ)	2004	200	25,50	9,00	2,40	2600	35.0
(ex Afon Alaw-08)							
AK TUE (KAZ)	2008	156	25,10	10,00	2,00	2600	28.0
(ex Dulas Island-08)							

Also operate other types of vessels

Coastal towage and marine civil engineering around Europe

IRONWHARF BOATYARD
Abbey Fields, Faversham, Kent, ME13 7BY
Tel : 01795 536296   Fax : 01795 532020
E-mail : office@ironwharfboatyard.fsnet.co.uk
Website : www.ironwharf.co.uk

PEP (GBR)	1951	24	16,58	3,96	1,82	152
(ex Placate-81)						

Towage services at the boatyard

ISLE OF MAN GOVERNMENT (HARBOURS DIV.)
Sea Terminal Building, Douglas, Isle of Man, IM1 2RF
Tel : 01624 686628   Fax : 01624 626403
E-mail : enquiries@harbours.dot.gov.im
Website : www.gov.im/harbours
Livery - Black hull, white housing, white funnel with company emblem

TARROO USHTEY (IOM)	1997		15,00	6,00	1,50	600	6.0

Towage and marine services at Douglas and surrounding coastline

ITCHEN MARINE (TOWAGE) LTD
American Wharf, Marine Parade, Southampton, SO14 5JF
Tel : 023 8063 1500   Fax : 023 8033 5606
Livery - Black hull with light blue trim, buff housing and wheelhouse, red funnel with blue and black stripes

WYEFORCE (GBR)	1993	57	19,20	6,10	2,60	1348	18.3
WYEFUEL (GBR)	1973	90	18,28	5,25	2,59	330	3.3
(ex Norah-09)							
WYEPUSH (GBR)	1989	50	14,50	5,10	2,10	750	8.0
WYETOW (GBR)	1991	52	16,05	5,30	2,40	940	10.6

Also operate two smaller tugs WYEDAWAKE and WYEMOOR

Towage services at Southampton

Although tugs of Itchen Marine are based at Southampton, they do occasionally work elsewhere. On 27 July 2006, the WYETOW enters Portsmouth harbour.

(Chris Jones)

J F MARINE
The Chandlery, Rhu Marina, Rhu, Helensburgh, G84 8LH
Tel : 01436 820584
E-mail : office@jfmarine.co.uk
Website : www.jfmarine.co.uk

HYDRONAUT	(GBR)	1980	27	11,50	4,50	1,99	200	2.5

(ex Cobh-02)

Marine, towage and diving services around the Gareloch and west coast of Scotland

J SEAS MARINE SERVICES LTD
14 Greens Place, South Shields, NE33 2AE
Tel : 07736 821246
E-mail : jculley5@blueyonder.co.uk
Website : www.jseas5marineservices.com
Livery - Black hull, orange upperworks with yellow funnel

AMBER ROSE	(GBR)	1969	13,90	3,70	1,80	240

(ex Toward Venture-06, Margaret Isobell)

Towage and marine services mainly on River Tyne, River Wear and River Tees

JENKINS MARINE LTD

Unit 12, Dawkins Road Industrial Estate, Poole, Dorset, BH15 4JP
Tel : 01202 668558   Fax : 01202 669209
E-mail : office@jenkinsmarine.co.uk
Website : www.jenkinsmarine.co.uk

GLENESK (GBR)	1976	37	15,70	4,90	2,25	730	10.5
(ex Comar-99, Omar)							
POLMEAR (GBR)	2004	43	14,65	5,50	1,67	880	10.0
URSA (GBR)	1985	48	15,30	4,60	2,30	600	8.0
(ex Wyepull-08)							

Also operate barges and other types of vessels
Coastal towage around the UK and support of marine civil engineering

JERSEY HARBOURS

Maritime House, La Route du Port Elizabeth, St Helier, Jersey, JE1 1HB
Tel : 01534 447788   Fax : 01534 447799
E-mail : jerseyharbours@gov.je
Website : www.jersey-harbours.com

DUKE OF NORMANDY (GBR)	2005	161	26,21	9,10	2,60	2200	28.3

Towage and general marine services in Jersey and surrounding coast

KING'S LYNN CONSERVANCY BOARD

Harbour Office, Common Staith, King's Lynn, Norfolk, PE30 1LL
Tel : 01553 773411   Fax : 01553 763431
E-mail : harbourmaster@portauthoritykingslynn.fsnet.co.uk
Website : www.portauthoritykingslynn.fsnet.co.uk
Livery - Black hull with white wheelhouse with name on side

CONSERVATOR (GBR)	2003		16,65	5,29	2,30	1080	14.2

Towage and marine services at the port of King's Lynn

KLYNE TUGS (LOWESTOFT) LTD

Cumberland Place, Whapload Road, Lowestoft, Suffok, NR32 1UQ
Tel : 01502 515250   Fax : 01502 500225
E-mail : Enquiries@klyne-tugs.co.uk
Website : www.jpknight.com
Livery - White hull with red and blue 'coastguard' stripe, cream housing, buff funnels 'KTL'
in green letters

ANGLIAN MONARCH (GBR)	1998	1485	58,00	14,10	6,90	11400	152.0
ANGLIAN PRINCE (GBR)	1980	1598	69,06	14,86	6,14	11280	170.0
(ex Hispania-96, Salvageman-91)							

The ANGLIAN PRINCESS left her usual station in the South-West Approaches in late May 2008 and put on a fine display at an open day in Milford Haven on 31 May.

(Steve Kerrison)

ANGLIAN PRINCESS	(GBR)	2002	2270	67,40	15,50	6,20	16500	180.0
ANGLIAN SOVEREIGN	(GBR)	2003	2500	67,40	15,50	5,20	16092	180.0

MCA Emergency Towing Vessels

Now part of the J P Knight Group and trading as J P Knight (Anglian) Ltd

J P KNIGHT (CALEDONIAN) LTD
37 Shore Road, Invergordon, Ross-shire, IV18 0EH
Tel : 01349 852611   Fax : 01349 853087
E-mail : tugs@jpknight.co.uk
Website : www.jpknight.com
Livery - Red and black hull, brown housing and white wheelhouse, black funnel with white K

KEVERNE	(GBR)	2006	393	32,50	11,40	4,40	4500	65.0
(ex Azuma Maru-07)								
KINDEACE *	(GBR)	2005	394	32,50	11,40	4,40	4400	64.0
(ex Fuji Maru-07)								
KINTORE	(GBR)	2006	393	32,50	11,40	4,40	4500	65.0
(ex Iide Maru-07)								

* on long-term bareboat charter to Multratug for service with Antwerp Towage NV, and renamed MULTRATUG 5.

Towage services on the Cromarty Firth

The KINTORE passes through the Fair Isle Gap on 27 August 2007.

(Richard Jones)

J P KNIGHT GROUP LTD
The Admiral's Offices, Chatham Historic Dockyard, Kent, ME4 4TZ
Tel : 01634 826633   Fax : 01634 829093
E-mail : navigators@jpknight.com
Website : www.jpknight.com
Livery - Black hull with white housing, black funnel with white K

KENLEY (VCT)	1996	327	25,96	9,57	3,04	2400	n/a
(ex EMS Express-04, Mack)							
KENNET (VCT)	1981	282	24,26	8,32		4800	n/a
(ex Terese Marie)							
KESSOCK (GBR)	1975	233	28,35	9,35	3,88	2400	35.0
KUTARI (VCT)	1991	192	18,00	9,47	2,40	2500	n/a

Towage and pusher services in South America

LAXEY TOWING COMPANY LTD
Overstone's Cottage, Balderine Hill, Balderine, Isle of Man, IM4 6DS
Tel / fax : 01624 861724
Livery - Black hull with brown housing, white wheelhouse, black/white/red funnel with
black L on white band

WENDY ANN (GBR)	1934	72	23,10	5,48	2,24	600	8.0
(ex Vespa-74, Evelene Brodstone-46, Brodstone-35)							
LONAN (GBR)	1976	8	9,14	3,35	1,37	200	3.0
(ex Lagan-99, Veronica-98)							

Towage and marine services at Isle of Man ports

LERWICK PORT AUTHORITY
Albert Building, Lerwick, Shetland, ZE1 0LL
Tel : 01595 692991   Fax : 01595 693452
E-Mail : info@lerwick-harbour.co.uk
Website : www.lerwick-harbour.co.uk
Livery - Black hull with white housing

KEBISTER (GBR)	1990	143	24,00	7,60	3,85	1760	24.0
KNAB (GBR)	2006	118	20,00	7,40	3,60	1440	21.0

Towage services at Lerwick

D LITTLE ENGINEERING LTD
The Barn, Summer Hill, Freystrop, Haverfordwest, SA62 4LQ
Tel : 01437 890804   Fax : 01437 891315
E-mail : davelittle@btinternet.com
Website : www.dlittleengineering.co.uk
Livery - Black hull with white wheelhouse

INTREPID B (GBR)	1997/02	181	27,00	8,80	5,50	1285	20.0
(ex Harvest Reaper III-01)							

Marine services around Europe and coastal towage

PORT OF LONDON AUTHORITY
London River House, Royal Pier Road, Gravesend, Kent, DA12 2BG
Tel : 01474 562200   Fax : 01474 562281
Website : www.pla.co.uk
Livery - Green hull, cream wheelhouse with orange band around top of wheelhouse

IMPULSE (GBR)	1995	52	14,00		1,50	470	5.6

Towage and marine services on the River Thames

LONDONDERRY PORT & HARBOUR COMMISSIONERS
Harbour Office, Port Road, Lisahally, Londonderry, BT47 1FL
Tel : 028 71860555   Fax : 028 71861168
E-mail : info@londonderry-port.co.uk
Website : www.londonderryport.com
Livery - Blue hull with white wheelhouse

COULMORE (GBR)	1982	290	33,18	9,63	4,17	2640	42.0
(ex Ganges-05)							
OTTERBANK (GBR)	1996	120	16,89	5,29	2,51	800	11.4
SHROVE (GBR)	2000	112	17,00	8,00	4,45	2636	34.0
(ex Bergslep-03)							

Harbour towage and pilot boat services at Londonderry

MACDONALD FERRIES

West Harbour, Invergordon, Ross Shire, IV18 0EX
Tel : 01349 853669   Fax : 01349 854116
E-mail : info@macdonaldferries.co.uk
Website - www.macdonaldferries.co.uk

MERLIN (GBR)	1975	11,88				290	2.0
(ex Gael Vision)							
PIONEER (GBR)	1955	19,20	4,87	1,82		400	4.0

Also operate barges and smaller tugs/workboats
Marine services around Cromarty and Moray Firths and the Caledonian Canal

MANCHESTER SHIP CANAL COMPANY

Engineering Workshops, Percival Lane, Runcorn, Cheshire, WA7 4UY
Tel : 01928 508550   Fax : 01928 567469
E-mail : mail@shipcanal.co.uk
Website : www.shipcanal.co.uk

M.S.C. DAINTY (GBR)	1960	37	16,76	4,05	2,30	143
M.S.C. DAWN (GBR)	1960	37	16,76	4,05	2,30	143

Marine services on the Manchester Ship Canal

MANOR MARINE

Portland Port Business Centre, Castletown, Portland, Dorset, DT5 1PB
Tel : 01305 820777   Fax : 01305 824300
E-mail : mpiservices@manormarine.co.uk
Website : www.manormarine.co.uk

CHIMERA (GBR)	1880	42	19,50	3,80	2,20	400
(ex Cito 1, Munkholmen, Vildanden, Skjelsvik)						

Marine services around the port of Portland

MAGNUS GROUP

Cliff Reach, Cliff Road, Ipswich, Suffolk, IP3 6PB
Tel : 01473 281888   Fax : 01473 226743

TAYRA (GBR)	1958	69	20,00	7,50	2,80	500	7.5
(ex Abeille 13-87, Patmore, Tayra)							

Towage services at the port of Ipswich

MARINECO UK LTD

The Steading, Pentland Mains, Edinburgh, EH20 9QG
Tel : 0131 445 2345   Fax : 0131 445 4418
E-Mail : info@mcou.com
Website : www.mcouk.com
Livery - Black hull, yellow housing with white wheelhouse

MARINECO

ASHANTI (GBR)	2005	161	26,09	7,94	3,75	3500	50.7
(ex Kilp-08)							
MARINECO HATHI (GBR)	2008	154	24,00	9,00	2,40	1696	23.5
MARINECO INDIA (GBR)	1993	68	19,50	6,00	2,10	880	14.5
(ex Oil Randan-05)							
MARINECO							
TOOMAI (GBR)	2007	212	26,02	9,10	2,65	2228	30.0

Marine civil engineering around Europe

The MARINECO ASHANTI at anchor off Gibraltar on 7 November 2008.

(Simon Smith)

MARINE SERVICES (GRIMSBY) LTD
14 Denby Drive, Cleethorpes, North East Lincolnshire, DN35 9QQ
Tel : 07936 310384   Fax : 01472 604041
Livery - Black hull, white or red housing, white wheelhouse and black and white funnel

ESTE (GBR)	1973	196	29,67	8,06	2,65	1775	23.0
(ex Geeste-05, Midgard I-04)							
INGE (GBR)	1962	143	23,78	7,88	3,60	1000	11.5
(ex Stedingen-96)							
JADI (GBR)	1968	143	25,56	7,88	3,60	1000	11.5
(ex Butjadingen-96)							
KNAP (GBR)	1980	71	18,60	6,10	2,80	460	7.0
(ex Knab-06)							
LESLENE (GBR)	1958	100	24,28	6,52	3,20	600	7.0
(ex Carraig Dubh-93, Jan Goedkoop Jnr.-72)							

Harbour towage at Grimsby

The JADI assists a cargo vessel at Grimsby on 13 November 2008.

(Kevin Jones)

MARITIME CRAFT SERVICES (CLYDE) LTD

Largs Yacht Haven, Irvine Road, Largs, Ayrshire, KA30 8EZ
Tel : 01475 675338   Fax : 01475 689000
E-mail : charter@maritimecraft.co.uk
Website : www.maritimecraft.co.uk
Livery - Black hull, Baltic blue bulwarks, white housing

MCS AILSA (GBR)	1996	497	42,00	14,50	2,00		2000	22.0
(ex Katliz-03)								
MCS ALIX (GBR)	2006	161	26,08	9,10	2,60		2234	29.0
MCS ANIE (GBR)	2006	224	25,25	8,60	4,00		3040	42.4
(ex Dogancay XIII-07)								
MCS ANNEKE (GBR)	1999	94	20,20	8,04	1,81		1200	15,0
(ex Mariska V-01)								
MCS ELLY (GBR)	1997	196	25,80	10,15	2,30		1200	18,0
(ex DH Charlie-02)								
MCS HEATHER (GBR)	2005	224	25,25	8,60	3,10		3000	42.0
(ex Corvin-07, Dogancay X-05)								
MCS IRIS (GBR)	2006	224	25,25	8,60	4,00		3040	42.0
(ex Dogancay XIV-07)								
MCS LENIE (GBR)	2008	289	27,02	9,10			3000	39.5
MCS MARLENE (GBR)	2005	87	22,50	8,20	4,00		3000	45.0
(ex Alsancak 2-07)								
MCS NIKKI (GBR)	2004	161	26,08	9,10	2,60		2200	30,0

Coastal towage and marine civil engineering services

McCRAE MARINE SERVICES
Nigg, Tain, Ross-shire, IV19 1QU
Tel : 01631 740206

KATHLEEN	(GBR)	1972	50	18,28	5,26	2,59	330	3.3

Also operate the small line-handling tug SWORDFISH
Marine services in the Cromarty Firth

JOHN McLOUGHLIN & SON (SHIPPING) LTD
North End, Larne Harbour, Larne, Co. Antrim, Northern Ireland, BT40 1AJ
Tel : 028 2827 3785   Fax : 028 2826 0382
E-mail : mail@johnmcloughlinshipping.co.uk
Website : www.johnmcloughlinshipping.co.uk
Livery - Orange hull with white lettering, white housing, orange funnel with two white bands

tbn	(GBR)	2009		16,00	6,20		1600	20.0
ADRIENNE McLOUGHLIN	(GBR)	1970	16	11,00	3,75	1,50	175	2.0
DAVID McLOUGHLIN	(GBR)	1971	22	14,00	3,75	1,75	250	6.0
DEIRDRE McLOUGHLIN	(GBR)	1980	16	11,00	3,50	1,75	175	3.0
LEANNE McLOUGHLIN	(GBR)	2005	32	15,00	4,00	2,10	400	6.0
MARIA McLOUGHLIN	(GBR)	1981	35	16,00	4,50	2,10	500	8.0
MARY-ANN McLOUGHLIN	(GBR)	1972	21	14,00	3,75	1,00	150	1.5
MICHAEL McLOUGHLIN	(GBR)	1978	39	16,33	5,01	2,60	624	10.0

(ex Maura-04, Argus B-00, Glenesk-98)

NOLEEN McLOUGHLIN	(GBR)	2005	32	15,00	4,00	2,10	400	6.0
SARAH McLOUGHLIN	(GBR)	1981	35	16,00	4,50	2,10	500	8.0

Towage and line-handling services in Belfast, Belfast Lough and Port of Larne

MEDWAY PORTS AUTHORITY
Sheerness Docks, Sheerness, Kent, ME12 1RS
Tel : 01795 596596   Fax : 01795 680072
E-mail : cathrynspain@medwayports.com
Website : www.medwayports.com
Livery - Black hull and housing with orange wheelhouse

MEDWAY OTTER	(GBR)	1973	21	15,50	4,30	1,75	153	0.8

Marine services on the River Medway
Part of the Peel Ports Group

MEDWAY TOWING SERVICES

Denton Slipways, Wharf Road, Gravesend, Kent, DA12 2RU
Tel : 01474 536173
Livery - Black hull, brown housing with white wheelhouse, green funnel with white band

MERANO	(GBR)	1949/66	23	13,00	3,90	1,46	120	3.0

(ex Request-53, Falgarth-50)

SILVERBEAM	(GBR)	1951	92	25,51	6,40	2,93	800	9.0

(ex Jean Raby-03, Mercedes II-83, Silverbeam-70)
Light towage services on the River Medway and River Thames

The SILVERBEAM at work in the River Thames on 28 October 2008.

(Krispen Atkinson)

MILFORD HAVEN PORT AUTHORITY

Gorsewood Drive, Hakin, Milford Haven, SA73 3ER
Tel : 01646 696100   Fax : 01646 696125
E-mail : enquiries@mhpa.co.uk
Website : www.mhpa.co.uk
Livery - Black hull, dark blue housing and white wheelhouse
Operated by Milford Docks

LILAH	(GBR)	1973	50	18,28	5,26	2,59	330	3.3

Towage services in Milford docks

MISTLEY MARINE & LEISURE LTD

Northumberland Wharf, Anchor Lane, Mistley, Manningtree, Essex, CO11 1NG
Tel : 01206 392127   Fax : 01206 396952
E-mail : davidfoster@aol.com

MERLIN	(GBR)	2005		20,00	7,50	1,50	550	8.0

Also operate a fleet of barges
Marine services on the east coast of England

MTS (MARINE & TOWAGE SERVICES) GROUP LTD

The Docks, Falmouth, Cornwall, TR11 4NR
Tel : 01326 312987   Fax : 01326 312564
E-mail : falmouth@mtsgroupltd.com
Website : www.mtsgroupltd.com
Livery - Black hull with orange bulwarks; white wheelhouse

BAY PROTECTOR		1967/87	114	26,19	6,10	2,80	750	10.0
(ex Protector-95, HD 91-89, Wouter Johannis-84)								
MTS INDUS	(NLD)	1964/03	97	25,26	6,80	3,00	1775	24.4
(ex Indus-09)								
MTS TAKTOW	(GBR)	1981/07	109	22,50	6,80	3,00	1220	18.2
(ex Taktow 1-07)								
MTS VALIANT	(NLD)	2008	221	27,02	9,65	2,50	3000	40.0
MTS VALID	(NLD)	1981/06		13,00	4,00	1,50	375	4.0
(ex Trio-06)								
MTS VALOUR	(GBR)	2006	126	23,35	8,65	2,10	1720	23.0
(ex DMS Heron-06)								

The MTS VALOUR was one of many tugs to assist in salvage work on the stricken MSC NAPOLI.
She was photographed in Lyme Bay on 7 February 2007.

(Dominic McCall)

MTS VENGEANCE (GBR) 1988 156 24,50 7,80 3,60 2100 30.0
(ex Fairplay 10-07, Lady Sybil-99)
MTS VICTORY (GBR) 2009 23,50 8,35 3,50 2028 40.0
MTS VIXEN (GBR) 1969/08 22,50 6,80 3,00 595 8.8
(ex Doris K-08, Doris-90)
MTS VULCAN (GBR) 1998/07 14,00 5,00 1,60 525 6.0
(ex Kathy M-07)
Towage and marines around the south coast of England

MURPHY MARINE SERVICES LTD
89 The Drive, Morden, Surrey, SM4 6DH
KIERA G (GBR) 1953 27 14,02 3,35 2,07 280
(ex Cubow-05, Kenneth G)

N E MURRAY MARINE CONTRACTORS
8 Rushenden Road, Queenborough, Kent, ME11 5HB
Tel : 01795 580998   Fax : 01795 665534
E-mail : ken@murraytugs.com
Website : www.murraytugs.com
Livery - Black hull, white housing and wheelhouse, red funnel
NORE
    CHALLENGER* (COM) 1973 184 31,91 8,84 3,51 1800 32.0
(ex Superbe-00, Guarne-78)
NORE
    COMMODORE (BLZ) 1961 147 28,65 7,73 2,89 1318 16.0
(ex Towfish-96, Airedale-95)
NORE SWALE (GBR) 1955 119 28,45 7,73 2,54 1080 12.0
(ex Prestwick-00)
NORE TRITON (GBR) 1964 50 16,70 5,30 2,80 500 5.0
(ex Zephyr)
PIONEER (COM) 1967 231 33,02 8,97 3,97 2250 35.0
(ex Sandsfoot Castle-03, Elena B-96, Afon Goch-91, Karet-82)
SEA TRACTOR (GBR) 1977 15,25 4,57 1,68 400 4.0
    Based Ramsgate for ferry berthing and coastal towage, flies Comoros Islands flag
Other tugs provide towage services on the Rivers Medway and Thames, also coastal towage

NORTH WESTERN STEAMSHIP CO LTD
Tel : 0151 334 6715
E-mail : info@tugkerne.co.uk
Website : www.tugkerne.co.uk
KERNE (GBR) 1912 63 23,47 5,48 2,59 400 n/a
(ex Terrier-47, Viking-13)
Preserved steam tug based at Ellesmere Port Boat Museum

The PIONEER at Newhaven on 3 February 2007.

(Phil Kempsey)

The OSPREY FIGHTER was photographed in the Clyde estuary on 9 April 2008.

(Danny Lynch)

OFFSHORE WORKBOATS LTD
River Clyde Boatyard, Rothesay Dock East, Clydebank, Dumbartonshire, G81 1YP
Tel : 0141 941 3366   Fax : 0141 941 3344
Website : www.clydeboatyard.co.uk

BARROW SAND (GBR)	1970	79	19,50	6,70	1,70	620	6.5
DONNA (GBR)	1975	35	16,10	4,00	2,00	380	7.0
(ex Donna McLoughlin-07)							
TRIO (GBR)	1972		14,50	4,30	1,80	380	4.2

Towage and marine services on the River Clyde

ORKNEY ISLANDS COUNCIL
Department of Harbours, Harbour Authority Building, Scapa, Orkney, KW15 1SD
Tel : 01856 873636   Fax : Tel : 01856 873012
E-mail : harbours@orkney.gov.uk
Website : www.orkneyharbours.com

KIRKWALL BAY (GBR)	1992	57,00	17,25	5,19	2,00	899	9.5

Towage and pilot launch services at Kirkwall

ORKNEY TOWAGE COMPANY LTD
Harbour Authority Building, Scapa, Orkney, KW15 1SD
Tel : 01856 873636   Fax : 01856 877635
E-mail : orkney.towage@orkney.gov.uk
Website : www.orkneyharbours.com
Livery - Black hull with white housing, buff funnel with company emblem & a red main mast

EINAR (GBR)	1989	410	31,50	10,00	4,78	4000	53.0
ERLEND (GBR)	1990	410	31,50	10,00	4,78	4000	53.0
HARALD (GBR)	1992	411	32,00	10,00	4,78	4000	55.0

Towage services at Flotta oil terminal in Scapa Flow. Coastal towage around Scotland.

OSPREY SHIPPING LTD
Unit 4A, Morston Quays, Wallsend, Tyne & Wear, NE28 6UE
Tel : 0191 234 5511   Fax : 0191 234 0888
E-mail : pete.fletcher@osprey.ltd.com
Website : www.ospreyltd.com
Livery - Red hull, orange housing and white wheelhouse, yellow funnel with 'OSPREY' written in black vertically

CUMBRAE (GBR)	1961	152	28,65	7,39	3,66	1320	16.1
(ex Clutha-97, Alsatian-95)							
Livery - Dark blue hull, white upperworks							
OSPREY							
FIGHTER (VCT)	2007	318	27,70	9,80	4,01	3600	50.0

Also operate a fleet of flat-top barges

Coastal towage on the east coast of England

PALMER MARINE SERVICES
Katrina Wharf, Wharf Road, Gravesend, Kent, DA12 2RU
Tel : 01474 352582
Livery - Black hull with green housing and white wheelhouse, blue funnel with large white P

CHIEFTON (GBR)	1963	37	18,74	5,18	2,29	495	6.5
(ex Seamaid-06, Barbara-82)							
UNICO (GBR)	1927	51	17,70	4,75	2,13	200	3.0

Marine services on the River Thames and River Medway

PERTH & KINROSS COUNCIL
Harbour Office, Friarton Road, Perth, PH2 8BB
Tel : 01738 624056   Fax : 01738 622263
E-mail : dhgibson@pkc.gov.uk
Website : www.pkc.gov.uk/harbourshipping

FAIR MAID						
OF PERTH (GBR)	2007	13,00	5,40	1,90	660	9.4

Marine services around Perth and on the River Tay

The FAIR MAID OF PERTH at the builder's yard in Macduff on 22 March 2007.

(David Dodds

PETERHEAD PORT AUTHORITY
Harbour Office, West Pier, Peterhead, AB42 1DW
Tel : 01779 483600   Fax : 01779 475715
E-mail : capt.hemingway@peterheadport.co.uk
Website : www.peterheadport.co.uk
Livery - Blue hull with white trim and white wheelhouse

FLYING SCUD	(GBR)	1981	18	11,30	3,60	1,50	127	1.0
UGIE RUNNER	(GBR)	2008		13,00	5,40	2,40	700	9,5

Towage services around Peterhead Port

POOLE HARBOUR COMMISSIONERS

20 New Quay Road, Hamworthy, Poole, Dorset, BH15 4AF
Tel : 01202 440200   Fax : 01202 440212
E-mail : pooleharbourcommissioners@phc.co.uk
Website : www.phc.co.uk
Livery - Dark green hull with yellow housing and white wheelhouse
HERBERT

BALLAM	(GBR)	1997	64	18,00	6,00	2,40	1300	18.0

Towage services at Poole

PORT EDGAR MARINA & SAILING SCHOOL

Shore Road, South Queensferry, West Lothian, EH30 9SQ
Tel : 0131 331 3330   Fax : 0131 331 4878
E-mail : info.pem@edinburghleisure.co.uk
Website : www.edinburghleisure.co.uk   Then select "Sailing & Watersports"

THUMPER	(GBR)	1997		15,00			770	7.0

Marine services around Port Edgar Marina

PORT TALBOT DIVING & MARINE

45 Sitwell Way, Port Talbot, South Wales, SA12 6BP
Tel : 01639 884766   Fax : 01792 459550
E-mail : Enquiries@PTMarine.co.uk
Website : www.ptmarine.co.uk
Livery - Black hull, red wheelhouse with white trim

ALEC D	(GBR)	1960	130	18,28	10,97	1,80	1000	12.0
BOY EUAN	(GBR)	1972	20	11,23	4,18	1,60	240	2.0
G-WIZ	(GBR)	1974	25	15,24	4,34	1,90	480	6.0
(ex G.W. 226-96)								
STRATHDOON	(GBR)	1980	31	18,23	5,18	2,80	380	6.0
V-RON			7	8,10	3,10		120	1.0

Towage and marine services at Port Talbot

PORTLAND HARBOUR AUTHORITY LTD

Post Office, Portland Port, Castletown, Portland, DT5 1PP
Tel : 01305 824044   Fax : 01305 826143
E-mail : marine@portland-port.co.uk
Website : www.portland-port.co.uk
Livery - Black hull with white housing and wheelhouse

RUFUS CASTLE	(GBR)	1963	152	28,65	7,39	3,66	1320	16.1

RUFUS CASTLE   (GBR)   1963   152   28,65   7,39   3,66   1320   16.1
(ex Bassett Hound-98, Bassett-95, Beagle-65)
SANDSFOOT
  CASTLE   (GBR)   1965   152   28,65   7,39   3,66   1320   16.1
(ex Dalmatian-03)
WYKE CASTLE   (GBR)   1980   179   26,03   7,95   2,39   1600   27.0
(ex Pullman-04, Kiso Maru-03)
Harbour towage at Portland, also coastal towage

Portland"s tug fleet in its home port on 21 February 2007.

(Dominic McCall)

JOHN RHODES
6 Pullens Road, Painswick, Stroud, GL6 6QZ
Tel : 01452 812709
RESOLUTE LADY   (GBR)   1897   62   20,42   4,87   2,56   364
(ex Thelm Leigh-78, Resolute-70)
Vessel being restored on the River Severn

RIVER TEES ENGINEERING & WELDING LTD
The Slipways, Normanby Wharf, Middlesbrough, Cleveland, TS3 8AT
Tel : 01642 226226   Fax : 01642 245544
E-mail : river-tees@the-slipways.fsnet.co.uk
Website : www.river-tees-engineering.com
LIBRA STAR   (GBR)   1965   43   18,00   5,00   1,83   260   5.0
(ex Arco Deben-92, Walborg)
Marine services on the River Tees

ROSYTH MARINE SERVICES LTD
Building 1058, Middle Jetty Road, Rosyth Royal Dockyard, Fife, KY11 2YD
Tel : 01383 422450   Fax : 01383 423184
E-mail : tugs2000@rosyth.fsbusiness.co.uk
Livery - Red hull with white housing and wheelhouse
          Black hull with blue housing, white funnel (Babcock vessels)

ISABEL	(GBR)	1972	50	18,28	5,26	2,59	330	3.3
ST. MARGARET	(GBR)	1967	143	26,52	7,68	3,20	1200	15.0

(ex Inchcolm-89)

Managed for Babcock Rosyth Defence Ltd (UK)

DEERHOUND	(GBR)	1966	151	28,68	7,72	3,20	1770	17.0
ELKHOUND	(GBR)	1966	151	28,68	7,72	3,20	1770	17.0

Towage services at Rosyth

SCOTTISH MARITIME MUSUEM
Harbourside, Irvine, Ayrshire, KA12 8QE
Tel : 01294 278283   Fax : 01294 313211
E-mail : www.scottishmaritimemuseum.org

GARNOCK	(GBR)	1956	78	23,91	6,68	2,49	324	n/a

Preserved tug berthed at Irvine

SCRABSTER HARBOUR TRUST
Harbour Office, Scrabster, Caithness, KW14 7UJ
Tel : 01847 892779   Fax : 01847 892353
E-mail : harbour@scrabster.co.uk
Website : www.scrabster.co.uk

VENTURE	(GBR)	1976	15	36,88	11,75		189

(ex Kestrel Venture, Gael Venture)

Pilotage services at the port of Scrabster and occasional towage of small vessels

SEABORN CONTAINER LINE
Nelson Mill, Gaskell Street, Bolton, BL1 2QS

DAISY DOARDO	(GBR)	1964	42	18,48	9,82		1220

(ex Volito-07, Magdalena-05, Danielle, Breedu-92, Lotus-89, Lehnkering11-86,
   built as Lehnkering 108)

Pusher tug used on the River Mersey and Manchester Ship Canal

SEACOR MARINE INTERNATIONAL LTD
Columbus Buildings, Waveney Road, Lowestoft, Suffolk, NR32 1BN
Tel : 01502 573366   Fax : 01502 581500
E-mail : info.lowestoft@ckor.com
Website : www.seacormarine.com

PLANTER	(GBR)	1967	38	16,76	4,57	2,60	420	5.0

Towage services at the port of Lowestoft

The PLANTER berthed at Lowestoft on 10 February 2008.

(Dominic McCall)

SEAHAM HARBOUR

Cargo Durham Distribution Centre, Seaham, Co. Durham, SR7 7NZ
Tel: 0191 516 1700   Fax: 0191 516 1701
E-mail : info@seahamharbour.com
Website : www.victoriagroup.co.uk
Livery - Light blue hull, white wheelhouse with buff mast

SEAHAM PRIDE	(GBR)	1975	42	15,69	4,68	1,40	720	7.2

(ex Boy Henry-80)

Towage services at Seaham

SEAHORSE AQUACULTURE

Mellon Charles, Aultbea
Tel : 01445 731411

DAVID ANDREWS	(GBR)	1970	54	18,60	5,80	2,50	525	6.5

Also operate the smaller workboat TIE VENTURE III

Marine service to the fish farming industry on the west coast of Scotland

SERCO-DENHOLM MARINE SERVICES LTD

Great Harbour, Greenock, Inverclyde, PA15 2AR
E-mail : generalenquiries@serco.com
Website : www.serco.co.uk

Tel : Head Office, Portsmouth, 023 9272 7495
Devonport 01752 554193
Portsmouth 023 9272 2880
Clyde 01475 731540
Livery - Black hull with buff housing and red funnel with company logo

GWENDOLINE P (GBR)	1974	143	21,95	6,40	2,59		615	5.7
(ex Gwendoline-99)								
SD ADEPT (GBR)	1980	384	38,82	9,24	3,40		2640	29.6
(ex Adept-08)								
SD ATLAS (GBR)	1999	168	21,30	7,80	2,40		2100	33.0
(ex Yenikale-05)								
SD BOUNTIFUL (GBR)	2010		29,19	9,98	4,80		4023	40.0
SD BUSTLER (GBR)	1981	384	38,82	9,24	3,40		2640	29.6
(ex Bustler-08)								

The SD BUSTLER assists the SIR BEDIVERE out of Portsmouth on 19 November 2008.

(Bernard McCall)

SD CAPABLE (GBR)	1981	384	38,82	9,43	2,48		2640	29.6
(ex Capable-08)								
SD CAREFUL (GBR)	1982	384	38,82	9,43	2,48		2640	29.6
SD CATHERINE (GBR)	2007		12,26	3,80	2,01		167	2.1
SD CHRISTINE (GBR)	2010		21,19	9,43				23.4
SD DEBORAH (GBR)	2010		21,19	9,43				23.4
SD DEPENDABLE (GBR)	2010		29,19	9,98	4,80		4023	40.0
SD DEXTEROUS (GBR)	1986	384	38,84	9,43	2,50		2640	29.6
(ex Dexterous-08)								
SD EILEEN (GBR)	2010		21,19	9,43				23.4

SD EMILY (GBR)	2008		12,26	3,80	2,01	167	2.1
SD ENGINEER (GBR)	1996	102	18,70	8,06	1,08	600	7.7
(ex Forth Engineer-08)							
SD FAITHFUL (GBR)	1985	384	38,82	9,43	2,50	2640	29.6
(ex Faithful-08)							
SD FLORENCE (GBR)	1980	143	21,95	6,40	2,59	615	5.7
SD FORCEFUL (GBR)	1985	384	38,82	9,42	3,40	2640	29.6
(ex Forceful-08)							
SD FRANCES (GBR)	1980	143	21,95	6,40	2,59	615	5.7
SD GENEVIEVE (GBR)	1980	143	21,95	6,40	2,59	615	5.7
SD GEORGINA (GBR)	1973	143	21,95	6,40	2,59	615	5.7
SD HELEN (GBR)	1974	143	21,95	6,40	2,59	615	5.7
SD HERCULES (GBR)	2009	200	26,61	8,44	3,40	2200	30.0
SD HUSKY (GBR)	1969	152	28,68	7,72	2,70	1320	16.1
(ex Husky-08)							
SD IMPETUS (GBR)	1993	319	32,53	10,42	4,00	3400	38.6
(ex Impetus-08)							
SD IMPULSE (GBR)	1993	319	32,53	10,00	3,89	3400	38.6
(ex Impulse-08)							
SD INDEPENDENT							
(GBR)	2009		26,09	9,44		3480	40.0
SD INDULGENT (GBR)	2009		26,09	9,44		3480	40.0
SD INSPECTOR (GBR)	2001	91	18,70	8,06	1,76	601	7.8
(ex Forth Inspector-08, DMS Eagle-03)							
SD JUPITER (GBR)	2009	200	26,61	8,44	3,40	2200	30.0
SD KITTY (GBR)	1972	60	18,28	5,26	2,59	330	3.0
SD KYLE OF							
LOCHALSH (GBR)	1997	121	25,50	9,00	2,50	2200	28.0
(ex MCS Lenie-08)							
SD LESLEY (GBR)	1973	60	18,28	5,26	2,59	330	3.0
SD MARS (GBR)	2009	200	26,61	8,44	3,40	2200	30.0
SD MYRTLE (GBR)	1973	60	18,28	5,26	2,59	330	3.0
SD NAVIGATOR (GBR)	2009		26,27	10,64	2,55	957	12.5
SD NIMBLE (GBR)	1985	319	38,82	9,45	2,50	2640	29.6
(ex Nimble-08)							
SD POWERFUL (GBR)	1985	384	38,79	9,43	4,25	2640	29.6
(ex Powerful-08)							
SD RAASAY (GBR)	2010		26,27	10,64	2,55	957	12.5
SD RELIABLE (GBR)	2009		29,19	9,98	4,80	4023	40.0
SD RESOURCEFUL							
(GBR)	2010		29,19	9,98	4,80	4023	40.0
SD SHEEPDOG (GBR)	1969	152	28,65	7,39	3,66	1320	16.1
(ex Sheepdog-08)							
SD SPANIEL (GBR)	1967	152	28,65	7,39	3,66	1320	16.1
(ex Spaniel-08)							
SD SUZANNE (GBR)	2010		21,19	9,43			23.4
SD TILLY (GBR)	2009		14,53	4,98			8.0

Towage services for the Ministry of Defence around the UK

SHARPNESS SHIPYARD AND DRYDOCK LTD

The Docks, Sharpness, Gloucestershire, GL13 9UD
Tel : 01453 811261   Fax : 01453 811423
E-mail : info@sharpnessshipyard.com
Website : www.sharpnessshipyard.com

FREIGHT MOVER (GBR)	1968/74	38	16,66	4,70	3,50	426	3.0
(ex Plausible-74)							

SHOREHAM PORT

Nautilus House, 90-100 Albion Street, Southwick, Brighton, BN42 4ED
Tel : 01273 598100   Fax : 01273 592492
E-mail : info@shoreham-port.co.uk
Website : www.shoreham-port.co.uk
Livery - Blue hull with white wheelhouse and blue trim

ADURNI (GBR)	1984	40	15,70	4,80	2,20	720	10.0

Towage services at Shoreham

SILVERBURN SHIPPING (IOM) LIMITED

Unit 122, 8 Lombard Road, Wimbledon, SW19 3TZ
Tel : 020 8543 1124   Fax : 020 8540 6509
E-mail : chartering@silverburnshipping.co.uk
Website : www.silverburnshipping.co.uk
   Managed by Ark Shipping Ltd (Russia)

SOWENA (KAZ)	2000	294	36,00	9,00	3,50	2400	28.0
(ex Swissco Super-07)							
TARPAN (KAZ)	2008		42,00	12,50	3,50	5100	50.0
TEGEN (SKN)	1999	141	22,30	7,90	2,55	1780	24.0
(ex Dutch Pearl-07)							

Offshore operations in the Caspian Sea

SMIT HARBOUR TOWAGE

North Huskisson No.1 Dock, Regent Road, Liverpool, L3 0AT
Tel : 0151 9332151   Fax : 0151 9331700
E-mail : harbourtowage.liverpool@smit.com
Livery - Black with blue and yellow stripes on bow, white wheelhouse

SMIT BARBADOS (GBR)	2007	285	28,67	10,43	4,74	4930	59.2
SMIT COLLINGWOOD (GBR)	1981	281	30,64	9,33	2,66	2677	32.0
(ex Collingwood-07)							
SMIT DONAU (GBR)	2007	285	28,67	10,43	4,74	4930	59.2
SMIT LIVERPOOL (GBR)	1984	336	33,00	9,96	4,60	3493	38.0
(ex Bramley Moore-07)							
SMIT WATERLOO (GBR)	1987	298	31,15	9,76	3,40	3493	36.0
(ex Adsteam Waterloo-07, Waterloo-05)							

Towage services at Liverpool and on the River Mersey

One condition of the takeover of the former Adsteam fleet by Svitzer was that Adsteam's work on the River Mersey should not be included in that takeover. As a consequence, Smit Towage acquired Adsteam's Mersey tugs and this was the international company's first venture into harbour towage in the UK. The SMIT DONAU is one of two new vessels brought to the Mersey since that time and is seen passing Eastham on 13 February 2008.

(Bernard McCall)

SMIT INTERNATIONAL (SCOTLAND) LTD
Unit 1, Brunel Lock, Cumberland Basin, Bristol, BS1 6SE
Tel : 0117 952 9960   Fax : 0117 952 9969
E-mail : m.pope@smith.com
Website : www.smit.com
Livery - Black with blue and yellow stripes on bow, white wheelhouse

SMIT ARROL	(GBR)	2000	36	12,00	3,84	1,55	141	1.4
SMIT BAKER	(GBR)	2000	36	12,00	3,84	1,55	141	1.4
SMIT FOWLER	(GBR)	2000	36	12,00	3,84	1,55	141	1.4
SMIT YOUNG	(GBR)	2000	36	12,00	3,84	1,56	141	1.4

Line-handling services at the Hound Point oil terminal in the Firth of Forth

SMS TOWAGE LIMITED
Ocean House, Waterside Park, Livingstone Road, Hessle, HU13 0EG
Tel : 01482 350999   Fax : 01482 648284
E-mail : info@smstowage.com
Website : www.smstowage.com
Livery - Red hull and white housing with red funnel

ENGLISHMAN (GBR)	2006	329	28,00	9,80	4,00	3600	50.0
NORMAN (GBR)	1981	298	32,85	9,50	4,00	3200	50.0
(ex Nagato Maru-03)							
SERVICEMAN (GBR)	1984	194	31,35	9,50	3,20	3500	54.5
(ex Honzan Maru-03, Shinano Maru-03)							
TRADESMAN (GBR)	1987	131	22,60	8,50	3,70	2600	32.2
(ex Waglan-03)							
TRUEMAN (GBR)	1987	131	22,61	8,50	3,50	2600	32.2
(ex Tai Tam-03)							
WELSHMAN (GBR)	1998	292	31,00	9,80	3,50	3600	50.0
(ex Kincraig-09)							
On bareboat charter from HKST (Hong Kong)							
RISHMAN (HKG)	1989	188	24,00	8,50	3,50	3000	40.0
(ex Tsing Yi-06)							
YEOMAN (HKG)	1989	188	24,00	8,50	3,50	3000	40.0
(ex Tolo-06)							
Managed for REPASA (Spain)							
RED DOLPHIN (PMD)	2005	474	33,00	12,00	4,30	6472	82.0
(ex Remo-07)							
RED WOLF (ESP)	2006	500	33,00	12,00	4,30	6380	87.3

Towage services at Hull, Grimsby and Immingham; also coastal towage

The TRADESMAN assists a Polish bulk carrier at Hull on 10 October 2008.

(Kevin Jones)

SOLENT TOWAGE LIMITED

Esso Fawley Marine Terminal, PO Box 43, Hythe, Hampshire, SO45 1TF
Tel : 07970 940306   Fax : 07785 881170
E-mail : nick.jeffery@solenttowage.com
Website : www.solenttowage.com
Livery - Navy blue hull with light blue housing, navy blue funnel with white band and
company logo

APEX	(GBR)	2008	643	37,00	14,00	6,90	6758	67.0
ASTERIX	(GBR)	2001	31	13,00	4,80	1,90	552	9.5
IBEX	(GBR)	1993	33	14,40	4,73	1,50	600	7.6
PHENIX	(GBR)	2007	643	37,00	14,00	6,90	6850	67.0
TENAX	(GBR)	2006	643	37,00	14,00	6,90	6850	67.0
THRAX	(IOM)	1994	543	35,11	11,45	5,02	5000	62.0

Towage services at the Fawley oil terminal
Part of Østensjø Rederi AS

The TENAX assists the tanker GRENA at Fawley on 20 July 2006.

(Phil Kempsey)

THE SOUTH EASTERN TUG SOCIETY

Chatham Historic Dockyard, Chatham, Kent
Website : www.mtkent.org.uk

FEARNOUGHT	(GBR)	1966	16	12,80	3,35	1,52	110	n/a
KENT	(GBR)	1948	121	24,80	6,70	3,20	8,80	7,0

Preserved tug based on the River Thames but can be seen at various festivals

THE STEAM TUG PORTWEY TRUST
'Tether's End', Old London Road, Rawreth, Wickford, Essex, SS11 8UE
E-mail : portweytug@aol.com
Website-www.stportwey.co.uk
PORTWEY (GBR)   1927   94   24,54   5,48   2,74   330   n/a
Preserved tug berthed in West India Dock, London. Visits to the Rivers Thames and Medway made each year. Open on Wednesdays every week. Visitors welcome.

STEAM TUG TID 172
E-mail : tidtug@globalnet.co.uk
Website : www.users.globalnet.co.uk/~tidtug
TID 172 (GBR)   1946   54   22,55   5,18   1,82   220   n/a
Preserved steam tug berthed at Mistley, Essex

STENA LINE PORTS LTD
Stena House, Station Approach, Holyhead, Anglesey, Gwynedd, L65 1DQ
Tel : 01407 606666   Fax : 01407 606659
Livery - Black hull with white wheelhouse
ST DAVID (GBR)   2006   110   19,65   6,04   2,70   1440   21.0
(ex Valiant B-07)
Towage services at Holyhead assisting Stena ferries

The ELSA was photographed in the River Thames on 24 August 2008.

(Ed Gray)

MERVYN STREET
7 Hollytree Drive, Higham, Kent, ME3 7EG
Tel : 01474 822155
Livery - Orange hull and white upperworks

ELSA (GBR)	2006	19	13,00	5,40	1,80	1500	7.6

SUB MARINE SERVICES LTD
Western Wharf, The Docks, Falmouth, Cornwall, TR11 4NR
Tel : 01326 211517   Fax : 01326 211757
E-mail : info@submarineservices.com
Website : www.submarineservices.com
Livery - Black hull with dark yellow wheelhouse

JESSIE K (GBR)	1980	22	12,20	4,20	1,80	150	2.5
(ex Valour-02, Wyefuel-98)							
MARIANA K (GBR)	1971	20	14,45	4,28	1,80	365	4.0
(ex Mersey One-05, En Avant II-99, Heco-79)							

Marine civil engineering services around the UK

SULLOM VOE HARBOUR AUTHORITY
Port Administration Building, Sella Ness, Sullom Voe, Shetland, ZE2 9QR
Tel : 01806 242551   Fax : 01806 242237
E-mail : ports@shetland.gov.uk
Livery - Blue hull with white housing, black funnel

tbn (GBR)	2010		40,00	14,00	6,50	8810	77.0
tbn (GBR)	2010		40,00	14,00	6,50	8810	77.0
DUNTER (GBR)	1996	797	38,37	13,40	5,98	5760	56.0
SHALDER (GBR)	1983	482	37,33	11,30	5,40	4000	45.0
STANECHAKKER (GBR)	1978	392	37,25	10,00	5,40	3800	54.0
TIRRICK (GBR)	1983	482	37,33	11,30	5,40	4000	45.0
TYSTIE (GBR)	1996	797	38,37	13,40	5,98	5760	56.0

Towage services at Sullom Voe oil terminal

SVITZER MARINE LIMITED
Tees Wharf, Dockside Road, Middlesbrough, TS3 6AB
Tel : 01642 258300   Fax : 01642 246370
E-mail : hq@svitzer.com
Website : www.svitzer.com
Livery - Dark blue hull, cream housing and dark blue funnel with blue propeller symbol on cream band

Based at Grangemouth

FORTH (GBR)	1989	290	30,58	10,33	2,56	3382	37.0
(ex Cleveland Cross-02)							
ROSEBERRY							
CROSS (GBR)	1989	290	30,58	10,33	2,56	3382	37.0

Based on the River Tyne

PHOENIX CROSS (GBR)	1993	296	30,58	10,33	2,66	3890	42.0
ROWANGARTH (GBR)	1981	382	34,24	10,04	3,23	3200	42.0
YARM CROSS (GBR)	1979	207	28,30	9,00	2,76	2640	35.5

Based on the River Tees

COATHAM CROSS (GBR)	1981	207	28,30	9,00	2,76	2640	35.0

The COATHAM CROSS moves down the River Tyne on 21 June 2007.

(Dominic McCall)

FIERY CROSS (GBR)	1992	296	30,58	10,33	2,66	3890	42.0
ORMESBY CROSS (GBR)	2000	433	33,00	11,90	3,90	4400	55.0
SARAH D (GBR)	1978	210	24,50	8,50	2,00	800	10.0
(ex Cleveland Endeavour-01)							
SVITZER BOOTLE (GBR)	2003	366	29,50	11,45	5,90	4338	58.0
SVITZER SUN (GBR)	2008	203	24,47	10,70	5,31	5600	70.0

Based on the Humber Estuary

LADY STEPHANIE (GBR)	1984	285	30,21	9,73	4,61	2640	32.0
SVITZER ALMA (GBR)	1996	379	29,11	11,88	3,40	5600	59.0
(ex Lady Alma-07)							
SVITZER CONSTANCE (GBR)	1982	285	30,21	9,73	2,81	2640	32.0
(ex Lady Constance-07)							
SVITZER ELIZABETH (GBR)	1981	285	30,21	9,73	2,81	2640	32.0
(ex HT Sabre-08 Adsteam Elizabeth-06, Lady Elizabeth-05)							

SVITZER
ELLERBY   (GBR)   1998   267   29,70   9,60   3,75   3600   49.7
(ex Adsteam Ellerby-08, Lady Emma H-05, Lady Emma-98, Chek Chau-98)
SVITZER
FERRIBY   (GBR)   2005   243   24,55   11,49   5,40   5592   70.4
(ex Adsteam Ferriby-07)
SVITZER
JOSEPHINE   (GBR)   1991   364   30,58   11,50   3,40   4800   53.0
(ex Lady Josephine-07)
SVITZER
KATHLEEN   (GBR)   1991   364   30,58   11,50   3,40   4800   53.0
(ex Adsteam Kathleen-07, Lady Kathleen-06)
SVITZER KEELBY   (GBR) 1986   480   33,92   10,82   5,15   4800   61.0
(ex Adsteam Keelby-07, Redcliffe-05, W J Trotter-01)
SVITZER LAURA   (GBR) 2001   353   30,60   11,20   4,05   4800   70.0
(ex Adsteam Laura-07, Lady Laura-06)
SVITZER MOIRA   (GBR) 1998   267   29,70   9,60   3,75   4800   50.0
(ex Lady Moira-07, Peng-99, Peng Chau-99)
SVITZER SWORD   (GBR) 1982   339   30,72   9,50   3,80   2640   31.0
(ex HT Sword-09, Sun Thames-06)
SVITZER
VALIANT   (GBR)   2007   250   24,47   10,70   5,47   5600   69.0

The Svitzer company operates tugs in many parts of the world and has a policy of constant fleet renewal. This present listing provides an indication of the way that the company has expanded in the UK since the publication of the previous edition. SVITZER VALIANT is seen off Immingham on 16 February 2008.

(Simon Smith)

Based at Felixstowe and Harwich

SVITZER
BRIGHTWELL (GBR) 1986 256 28,80 9,05 4,06 3400 40.0
(ex Brightwell-07)
SVITZER
INTREPID (GBR) 2005 257 32,50 11,40 3,71 4400 60.0
(ex Adsteam Intrepid-07, Champion-07, Tadami Maru-07)
SVITZER MELTON (GBR) 1996 381 32,72 11,96 3,80 4825 61.0
(ex Melton-07)
SVITZER
SHOTLEY (GBR) 2006 243 24,55 11,59 5,40 5592 70.0
(ex Adsteam Shotley-08)

Based on the River Thames

LADY CECILIA (GBR) 1991 364 30,58 11,50 3,40 4800 53.6
LADY SUSAN (GBR) 1984 285 30,21 9,73 4,61 2640 32.0
SVITZER ANGLIA (GBR) 1985 336 33,00 9,50 4,72 3440 39.7
(ex Adsteam Anglia-08, Sun Anglia-06)
SVITZER LACEBY (GBR) 1990 364 30,58 11,50 3,40 4800 53.0
(ex Adsteam Laceby-07, Lady Anya-06)
SVITZER MERCIA (GBR) 1990 449 32,50 10,00 3,30 3860 42.6
(ex Adsteam Mercia-08, Sun Mercia-05)
SVITZER
REDBRIDGE (GBR) 1995 399 33,00 11,73 4,86 4104 45.0
(ex Adsteam Redbridge-08, Redbridge-05)
SVITZER
TRIMLEY (GBR) 1991 371 30,64 10,24 4,11 3860 43.0

Based on the River Medway

SVITZER BRENDA (GBR) 1985 360 38,00 10,27 3,20 3200 45.0
(ex Lady Brenda-08, Kenley-91, launched as Yokosuka Maru No. 2)
SVITZER HARTY (GBR) 2006 243 24,55 11,49 5,40 5592 68.0
(ex Adsteam Harty-07)
SVITZER MORAG (GBR) 1983 365 36,28 10,52 3,15 3400 50.0
(ex Adsteam Morag-09, Lady Morag-06, Kestrel-91, Kuroshio-91)
SVITZER
VICTORY (GBR) 2000 495 33,00 11,50 5,30 4894 65.0
(ex Adsteam Victory-07, Gurroung-05)
SVITZER WARDEN (GBR) 2006 243 24,55 11,49 5,40 5592 69.0
(ex Adsteam Warden-07)

Based at Southampton

ADSTEAM
LYNDHURST (GBR) 1996 379 30,00 11,60 3,80 4200 43.0
(ex Lyndhurst-06)
ADSTEAM
SURREY (GBR) 1992 399 30,10 10,50 4,67 3860 43.0
(ex Sun Surrey-05)
BENTLEY (GBR) 1996 381 32,72 11,96 4,25 4825 61.0
SVITZER
MADELEINE (GBR) 1996 381 32,72 11,96 3,80 4825 61.0
(ex Lady Madeleine-08)

Name		Year						
SVITZER SARAH	(GBR)	1991	364	30,58	11,50	3,40	4800	53.0
(ex Adsteam Sarah-07, Lady Sarah-06)								
SVITZER SUSSEX	(GBR)	1992	378	30,10	10,50	4,67	3860	43.0
(ex Adsteam Sussex-07, Sun Sussex-05)								
Based at Avonmouth/Portbury								
AVONGARTH	(GBR)	1980	241	32,07	9,20	2,50	2600	32.0
(ex Iwashima Maru-91)								
PORTGARTH	(GBR)	1995	262	30,70	10,04	4,10	3980	50.0
STACKGARTH	(GBR)	1985	216	28,29	8,95	4,80	3400	43.0
(ex Eston Cross-94)								
SVITZER BEVOIS	(GBR)	1985	250	29,37	9,12	4,58	2750	35.0
(ex Sir Bevois-07)								
SVITZER BRISTOL	(GBR)	2003	366	29,50	11,00	5,90	4338	60.0
SVITZER BRUNEL	(GBR)	2003	366	29,50	11,00	5,90	4338	60.0
SVITZER SKY	(GBR)	2008	203	24,47	10,70	5,31	5600	70.0

The SVITZER SKY, at the far right, was escorted by the SVITZER BRUNEL (left) and SVITZEF BRISTOL (centre) when she made her first arrival in the Bristol Channel on 20 February 2009.

(Bernard McCal

Name		Year						
Based at Newport/Cardiff/Barry								
BARGARTH	(GBR)	1979	225	28,43	8,92	2,97	2200	24.0
(ex Forth-03, Laggan-87)								
FLYING SPINDRIFT	(GBR)	1986	259	30,66	9,43	3,40	3100	38.0
HT CUTLASS	(GBR)	1984	287	30,10	9,22	3,23	2800	30.0
(ex Cobham-07, Dextrous-00)								

HT SCIMITAR (GBR)	1984	287	30,10	9,22	3,23	2800	30.0

(ex Shorne-06, Deft-00)

Based at Swansea/Port Talbot

DALEGARTH (GBR)	1985	360	38,00	10,27	3,15	3400	45.0

(ex Strongbow-91, Kestrel-90, Yokosuka Maru No. 1-85)

SHANNON (GBR)	1981	382	34,27	10,06	3,85	3200	42.0

(ex Eldergarth-99)

WESTGARTH (GBR)	1983	266	32,11	9,90	2,92	3000	40.0

(ex Yashima-92)

YEWGARTH (GBR)	1985	452	36,86	10,52	4,16	4000	50.0

Based at Milford Haven

ANGLEGARTH (GBR)	1996	374	32,72	11,96	4,95	5100	66.0
GRAY JUMBO (GBR)	1986	97	18,42	8,04	1,50	740	12.0
MILLGARTH (GBR)	1997	374	32,72	11,96	4,95	5100	66.0

The MILLGARTH in Milford Haven on 3 November 2008.

(Dominic McCall)

SVITZER CALDY (GBR)	2009	686	34,00	14,50	6,95	5900	80.0
SVITZER GELLISWICK (GBR)	2008	490	34,00	18,00	4,80	6000	80.0
SVITZER HAVEN (GBR)	2009	686	34,00	14,50	6,95	7880	92.0
SVITZER KILROOM (GBR)	2008	819	39,10	14,70	5,75	8182	110.0
SVITZER LINDSWAY (GBR)	2008	690	34,00	14,50	6,95	7714	96.0
SVITZER MALTBY (GBR)	2005	385	30,00	11,50	4,80	5700	70.0
SVITZER MUSSELWICK (GBR)	2008	490	34,00	18,00	4,80	6000	80.0

SVITZER RAMSEY (GBR)	2009	686	34,00	14,50	6,95	5900	80.0
SVITZER TAKU (GBR)	2008	592	12,80	4,50	1,50	610	8.0
SVITZER THAW (GBR)	2008	592	12,80	4,50	1,50	610	8.0
SVITZER THUNDER (GBR)	2007	592	12,80	4,50	1,50	610	8.0
SVITZER TORNADO (GBR)	2007	592	12,80	4,50	1,50	610	8.0

The year 2009 will see the commissioning of two new terminals on Milford Haven for the impor of liquefied natural gas. New tugs have arrived in the Haven to handle the large gas tankers anc six smaller vessels have been introduced mainly for line handling but with a useful bollard pu available if needed. The SVITZER THUNDER was photographed on 22 January 2009.

(Dominic McCall

SVITZER TORRENT (GBR)	2008	592	12,80	4,50	1,50	610	8.0
SVITZER TWISTER (GBR)	2008	592	12,80	4,50	1,50	610	8.0
SVITZER WATERSTON (GBR)	2008	686	34,00	14,50	6,95	7880	92.0
SVITZER WATWICK (GBR)	2008	490	34,00	18,00	4,80	6000	80.0
Based on the River Mersey							
ASHGARTH (GBR)	1992	307	36,50	10,20	3,30	3600	55.0
(ex Senho Maru-98)							
OAKGARTH (GBR)	1984	452	36,86	10,52	4,16	4000	50.0
SVITZER BIDSTON (GBR)	2004	366	29,50	11,00	5,90	4338	60.0
SVITZER STANLOW (GBR)	2006	637	37,50	13,50		7200	70.0

Name		Year							
THORNGARTH	(GBR)	1983	365	38,28	10,22	3,15	3400	45.0
(ex Tenzan-91)								

Based on the River Clyde

Name		Year							
AYTON CROSS	(GBR)	2000	433	33,00	11,90	3,90	4400	60.0
SVITZER MALLAIG	(GBR)	2005	385	30,00	11,50	4,80	5842	70.0
SVITZER MILFORD	(GBR)	2004	384	33,30	11,50	4,80	4820	66.0
WARRIOR III	(IRL)	1975	227	29,65	8,62	2,30	2600	35.0
(ex Celtic Warrior-96, Montenovo-93, Hakakuni Maru-91)								

Based at Belfast

Name		Year							
NORTON CROSS	(GBR)	1984	216	28,30	9,22	3,00	3400	43.0
WILLOWGARTH	(GBR)	1989	392	31,60	9,54	4,05	3400	45.0

Harbour towage around the UK and worldwide, also coastal towage

Part of the A P Møller - Mærsk Group. These tugs move between areas according to operational requirements.

The WARRIOR III and SVITZER MALLAIG assist a bulk carrier on to the berth at Hunterston on 25 July 2008.

(Dominic McCall)

SWANSEA MUSEUM

Victoria Road, Swansea, SA1 1SN
Tel : 01792 653763
E-mail : swansea.museum@swansea.gov.uk
Website : www.swanseaheritage.net

Name		Year							
CANNING	(GBR)	1954	200	31,60	7,80	3,58	825	n/a

Preserved tug berthed at Swansea Museum Pontoon, Swansea Marina

SWIFTSTONE TRUST

E-mail : info@thames.org.uk
Website : www.thames.org.uk

SWIFTSTONE	(GBR)	1952	91	24,38	5,90	2,92	660	8.2

Preserved tug moored on the River Thames

TALISMAN ENERGY (UK) LTD

Flotta Terminal, Flotta, Stromness, Orkney, KW16 3NP
Tel : 01856 884359
E-mail : flotta.shipping@talisman.co.uk
Livery - Black hull with lime green wheelhouse

GRAEMSAY LASS	(GBR)	1978	30	16,20	6,02	1,70	340	5.0
SWITHA LASS	(GBR)	1973	30	16,20	6,02	1,70	340	5.0

Marine services around Flotta oil terminal

TARGE TOWING LTD

Mountboy, Montrose, Angus, DD10 9TN
Tel : 01674 820234   Fax : 01674 820363
E-mail : ttl@targetowing.demon.co.uk
Livery - Black hull with white housing and red funnel

CARRICKFERGUS	(GBR)	1976	206	28,30	8,95	2,83	2200	27.0

(ex Greatham Cross-94)

The CARRICKFERGUS approaches Aberdeen on 12 August 2007. Although not seen in this view, she was towing the GRAMPIAN MONARCH which had broken down.

(Ashley Hunn)

CASTLE POINT**	(GBR)	2005	385	32,22	11,70	5,27	5310	66.7
COLLIE T	(GBR)	1964	152	28,65	7,39	3,65	1320	20.0
(ex Te Awhina-03, Collie-01)								
CORRINGHAM**	(GBR)	2005	385	32,22	11,70	5,27	5310	66.7
CULTRA	(GBR)	1976	206	28,30	8,95	2,83	2200	27.0
(ex Skelton Cross-93)								
STANFORD**	(GBR)	2005	385	32,22	11,70	5,27	5310	66.7
Managed for BP Exploration Operating Co Ltd (UK)								
CRAMOND*	(GBR)	1994	488	34,85	11,13	4,65	4800	62.0
DALMENY*	(GBR)	1994	488	34,85	11,13	4,65	4800	62.0
HOPETOUN*	(GBR)	1997	947	43,50	14,20	6,04	9700	124.0
Chartered for Strategic Operations Ltd (Bahamas)								
DEIDRE	(BHS)	1968	122	28,92	7,62	2,81	1500	23.0

Towage at Dundee, Aberdeen and Peterhead, also coastal towage
* *Towage services at Hound Point on the Firth of Forth*
** *Towage services at Coryton oil terminal on the River Thames*

TAYLOR & TAYLOR
The Harbour, Troon, KA10 6DW
Tel : 01292 315489   Fax : 01292 317276
E-mail : rdtaylorandtaylor@hotmail.com
Livery - Black and red hull with dark blue housing, white wheelhouse with red band at top

RED COUNTESS	(GBR)	1983	31	16,17	4,84	2,00	500	5.0
(ex Curlew-02)								
RED EMPRESS	(GBR)	1968	77	22,10	6,25	2,50	495	6.0
(ex Daphne B-03, Daphne-01)								

Towage services at Troon and barge operations on the west coast of Scotland

TECHNICAL MARINE SERVICES
West Acre, Chapel Lane, West Caister, Norfolk, NR30 5TA
Tel : 01493 728076
E-mail : tfarman@techmarineservices.co.uk
Website : www.techmarineservices.co.uk

SHEERKHAN	(GBR)	1976		17,50	6,00	1,80	640	8.0
(ex Marineco Sheerkhan-08, Le Gabion-07)								

TEIGNMOUTH HARBOUR COMMISSION
The Old Quay House, Old Quay, Teignmouth, Devon, TQ14 8ES
Tel : 01626 773165   Fax : 01626 778937
E-mail : info@teignmouthharbour.com
Website : www.teignmouthharbour.com
Livery - Light grey hull with white wheelhouse

TEIGN C	(GBR)	1997	27	14,40	4,73	1,70	600	8.5

Towage services at Teignmouth and local ports, also plough dredging

The TEIGN C is seen off her home port on 12 November 2005.

(Chris Jones)

BARRY TESTER
Hollowshore Boatyard, Faversham, Kent, ME13 7TU
Tel : 01795 532317

CHARLIGHT (GBR)	1936	13,72	3,73	1,30	115

THAMES & MEDWAY TOWAGE (SERVICES) LTD
13 Hayesford Park Drive, Bromley, Kent, BR2 9DA
Tel : 020 84603620   Fax : 020 83139488
Livery - Black hull, white housing and black, red and white funnel

AICIRTRON (GBR)	1967	109	22,08	6,84	3,50	890	12.0
(ex Smit Amerika-88, Bartel Wilton-84)							
GENERAL IX (GBR)	1940	74	21,00	5,49	3,00	420	
(ex Vista-75)							
WARRIOR (GBR)	1937	58	20,95	6,60	3,00	860	8.0
(ex General I-83, Vanoc-75)							

Towage services around the Thames estuary

THAMES TOWAGE
Nitricia, Benfleet Moorings, Ferry Road, Benfleet, Essex, SS7 1NS
Tel : 07711 846 060   Fax : 01268 684790
E-mail : brian@thames-towage.com
Website : www.thames-towage.com

ALA (GBR)	1965	45	19,00	5,48	2,43		450	3.6

(ex Herbert Crampin-87)
Also operate the small tug NITRICIA
Coastal towage around the UK

UK DREDGING
Queen Alexandra House, Cargo Road, Cardiff, CF10 4LY
Tel : 02920 835200   Fax : 02920 835216
E-mail : ukd@abports.co.uk
Website : www.ukdredging.co.uk
Livery : Dark blue hull with white wheelhouse
Managed for Associated British Ports Holdings plc

UKD SEAHORSE (GBR)	2000	206	25,97	10,06	2,45	1302	18.0
UKD SEALION (GBR)	2003	371	25,97	10,06	2,63	1279	17.6

Also operate a fleet of dredgers
Marine civil engineering and dredging support around the UK

The UK SEAHORSE was observed carrying out depth tests at Lowestoft on 9 February 2007.

(Ashley Hunn)

VIADUCT SHIPPING
9 Poulton Green Close, Spital, Bebington, Wirral, CH63 9FS
E-mail : lighterage@btclick.com
Livery - Black hull, buff upperworks and white wheelhouse; red funnel with black top
SEAPORT

ALPHA (GBR)	1943	54	20,42	5,79	1,82	280	5.5

(ex Tideall-86, TID 43-49)
Towage and marine services on the River Mersey and Manchester Ship Canal

WATERFRONT SERVICES

15-19 Corporation Square, Belfast, BT1 3AJ
Tel : 02890 90 242242
MICHAEL
    FRANCIS (GBR)   2000   16,89   5,29   2,24   940   13.0
Towage services at the port of Belfast

WILLIAMS MARINE & PORT SERVICES LTD

The Royal Dockyard, Port of Pembroke, Pembroke Dock, SA72 6TD
Tel : 01646 684169   Fax : 01646 687153
E-mail : info@wmps.co.uk
Website : www.wmps.co.uk
Livery - Blue hull with white trim and white wheelhouse
WMPS
    SEAHORSE (GBR)   1997   66   18,00   8,10   2,27   880   10.0
    (ex Seahorse-05)
    WILFREEDOM (GBR)   1989   47   19,36   6,17   2,05   883   11.4
    (ex Albatros 4-04, Albatros-03)
Towage and marine services at Milford Haven and in northern Europe
A joint venture by Williams Shipping Marine Ltd and The Milford Docks Company

Although nominally part of the Solent-based fleet, the WILLPOWER was photographed at the entrance to Milford Docks on 2 October 2006.

(Dominic McCall)

WILLIAMS SHIPPING MARINE LTD
Manor House Avenue, Millbrook, Southampton, SO15 0LF
Tel : 023 8052 9555   Fax : 023 8052 9444
E-mail : enquiries@williams-shipping.co.uk
Website : www.williams-shipping.co.uk
Livery - Blue hull with white trim and white wheelhouse

WILANNE	(GBR)	2004	36	16,89	5,29	2,25	940	12.8
WILCAT	(GBR)	1985	26	14,00	6,40	1,60	260	2.6
WILENDEAVOUR	(GBR)	2007		22,00	9,00	1,80	1200	15.0
WILKIT	(GBR)	2007		15,00	6,00	0,75	460	
WILLPOWER	(GBR)	1995	65	19,50	6,05	2,30	960	14,0

(ex Karin S-05, Diamante-98)
Also operate a fleet of flat-top barges
Towage services in Southampton Water and northern Europe

M V WINCHAM PRESERVATION SOCIETY LIMITED
7 Topgate Close, Heswall, Wirral, CH60 2UL
Tel : 0151 342 5468
E-mail : p.brown387@ntlworld.com

BROCKLEBANK	(GBR)	1965	172	31,37	8,26	3,00	1200	n/a

Preserved tug based at Liverpool but can be seen at various festivals

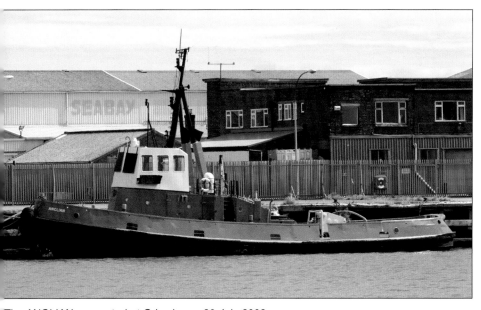

The ANGLIAN was noted at Grimsby on 20 July 2008.

(Simon Smith)

UNKNOWN OWNERS

ABERTAY   (GBR)   1967   184   30,33   8,44   3,48   1156   18.0
(ex Forth-84)

ANGLIAN (GBR)   1964   98   24,45   7,34   3,30   920   13.0
(ex Tugman-83)
Reported to be owned by Captain D Potter and K Dawson

BONCHURCH   (GBR)   1944   63   22,25   5,18   1,82   650   8.0
(ex Baie Comeau-66, Abeille No.13-63, TID 174)

CHARLOC   (GBR)   1962   42   18,90   5,20   385
(ex Charlock)

DOCKMAN   (GBR)   1949   68   20,76   5,95   650   8.0
(ex Alkelda-98, Dockman-93, Stamford Brook-63)

FIONA   (GBR)   1973   143   21,45   6,40   3,00   615   5.7

GARRY GRAY   (GBR)   1954   37   18,26   4,99   1,80   325   5.5
(ex Gary Gray, Lighterman-77, Jaycee-62)

GLUVIAS   (GBR)   1959   207   32,36   8,51   3,53   1260   22.0
(ex St Gluvias-05, Cruiser-81, Clonmel-73)

HECTOR READ   (GBR)   1965   67   19,80   5,80   2,60   545   6.3
Reported to be a houseboat at Port Werburgh, Hoo

HOFLAND   (GBR)   1964   36   16,36   4,78   2,30   380   4.2

IONIA   (GBR)   1960   187   30,41   7,98   3,53   1000   20.0
(ex St Mawes-05, Ionia-88)

JAMES WARD (GBR)   1948   26   15,21   4,02   1,82   210
Under restoration at Cuxton, River Medway

LOUISE B   1954   31   17,95   4,66   1,46   243
(ex Somme-78)

MAXIMUS   (GBR)   1956   141   29,00   7,10   3,20   750   8.0

MEECHING   (GBR)   1960   173   29,27   7,70   3,11   1320   16.0

OLIVER FELIX   1962   160   28,66   7,95   3,26   1080   14.5
(ex Luvly Jubbly-08, Oliver Felix-06, Polgarth-90)

PENDENNICK   (GBR)   1964   132   27,57   7,02   3,26   970   14.5
(ex Dunelm-88)

PLASHY (GBR)   1951   20   12,80   3,90   1,60   110

RIVERMAN   (GBR)   1955   37   17,34   4,98   1,80   324
(ex Rossend-05, Riverman-95, Bargeman-74, Brentonian-62)

ROSSLYN   (GBR)   1958   37   17,34   4,98   1,80   324
(ex Keelman-95, Scorcher-62)

SEA GRIFFON   (GBR)   1962   117   26,85   7,35   3,18   800   14.0

ST BUDOC (GBR)	1958	208	31,55	8,46	3,59	1270	18.0
(ex Foylegarth-83, Foylemore-69)							

Berthed at Sandbank Marina, Holy Loch, Firth of Clyde

ST PIRAN (SLE)	1960	316	39,07	9,05	3,70	1300	22.0
(ex Dalegarth-84)							

Reported to be owned by Captain D Potter and K Dawson

TORBROOK (GBR)	1958/77	13	12,19	3,05	1,52	120	1.4
(ex Tregarth-90, Shalldo-72)							

VANGUARD (GBR)	1965	306	38,71	9,12	3,78	1300	22.0
(ex Kenry-91, Campaigner-88, Rathgarth-77)							

VALID (GBR)	1990	21	12,80	4,20	1,70	280	3.5
VELOX (GBR)	1949	20	12,57	3,68	1,52	120	
WILLIAM RYAN (GBR)	1908	72	21,79	5,36	2,89	537	
(ex Toro-56)							

Reported to be a houseboat at Hoo Marina

TUGS - REPUBLIC OF IRELAND

BLUE OCEAN MARINE

Ferry Lodge, Bere Island, Beara, County Cork, Republic of Ireland
Tel : +353 27 75009   Fax : +353 27 75000
E-mail : biferry@eircom.net or info@bereislandferries.com
Website : www.bereislandferries.com

ADA DOROTHY (IRL)	1971	54	20,50	7,01	2,50	343	5.0
BLATH NA MARA (IRL)	1982	330	37,00	10,20		700	9.0
CAVA LASS (IRL)	1975	15	11,93	3,58	1,20	300	3.0
CHATEAU THIEREY (IRL)	1978	200	40,00	9,00	1,50	800	n/a
ENBANK (IRL)	1972	276	33,25	9,58	2,69	2800	30.0
(ex Schouwenbank-09)							
MADELEN (IRL)	1960	99	26,00	7,00	1,30	640	6.0
RYSA LASS (IRL)	1975	15	11,93	3,58	1,20	348	3.5
STENLAND (IRL)	1967	199	30,00	8,00	2,80		n/a
THOMAS F DOYLE (IRL)	1979	38	16,00			200	

Marine services, island cargo, tug and workboat hire, marine transport; also salvage in conjunction with Irish Diving Contractors, Lusk, County Dublin.

C W SHIPPING CO LTD

Fountain Cross, Ennis, County Clare, Republic of Ireland
Tel : +353 65 29470   Fax : +353 65 28316
SHANNON

ESTUARY I (IRL)	1956	176	30,18	8,21	3,12	1040	13.5
(ex Scotscraig-86, Flying Duck-76)							

Marine services in the Shannon estuary and along the west coast of Ireland

CARBERY ISLE FERRIES LTD
Baltimore, County Cork, Republic of Ireland

BARRACUDA BAY (GBR) 1970		13,30	4,00	1,50	220	3.0

Marine services around Baltimore

CASPIAN MAINPORT LTD
Monahan Road, Cork, Republic of Ireland
Tel : +353 1463 713323   Fax : +353 1463 233035
E-mail : george.macleod@caspianmainport.com
Website : www.caspianmainport.com
Livery - Green hull with wheelhouse

C M KURIK (CYM)	1995	129	23,62	9,00	2,20	1200	17.0

(ex Shoalbuster-07, Multrasalvor 2-06, Shoalbuster-04)

C M WULF (MHL)	1987	232	30,00	11,05	1,71	1266	18.2

(ex Taucher O. Wulf-08)

Marine services in the Caspian Sea

Part of Mainport Group

PORT OF CORK COMPANY
Custom House Street, Cork, County Cork, Republic of Ireland
Tel : +353 21 273125   Fax : +353 21 276484
E-mail : info@portofcork.ie
Website : www.portofcork.ie
Livery - Light blue hull with white housing

DENIS MURPHY (IRL)	2004	110	18,70	8,00	1,75	960	12.4
GERRY O'SULLIVAN (IRL)	1996	338	29,50	11,45	2,50	4100	46.0

Harbour towage at Cork

DROGHEDA PORT COMPANY
Maritime House, The Mall, Drogheda, County Louth, Republic of Ireland
Tel : +353 41.983 8378   Fax : +353 41 983 2844
E-mail : maritimehouse@droghedaport.ie
Website : www.droghedaport.ie

BOYNE PROTECTOR* (IRL)	2006	14,60	5,00	2,76	800	5.2

* no towing ring/hook, designed to push

Marine services at Drogheda

DUBLIN PORT COMPANY
Port Centre, Alexandra Road, Dublin 1, County Dublin, Republic of Ireland
Tel : +353 1 8876000   Fax : +353 1 8557400
E-mail : info@dublinport.ie
Website : www.dublinport.ie
Livery - Black and grey hull with buff housing and wheelhouse

tbn (IRL)	2009		24,00	11,00		5150	50.0
tbn (IRL)	2009		24,00	11,00		5150	50.0
BEN EADER (IRL)	1973	198	29,11	9,35	2,28	1620	16.0
CLUAIN TARBH (IRL)	1992	268	30,00	9,30	5,20	3440	36.5
DEILGINIS (IRL)	1996	335	29,50	11,00	3,40	3430	37.4

Harbour towage at Dublin

FASTNET SHIPPING LTD
Bridgewood House, Ballyrobin, Ferrybank, Waterford, Co Waterford Republic of Ireland
Tel : +353 51 832946   Fax : +353 51 851886
E-mail : fastnetshipping@eircom.net
Website : www.fastnetshipping.com

ADEPT (IRL)	1971	51	17,50	6,00	2,30	660	6.0
AGILE (IRL)	1971	51	17,50	6,00	2,30	660	6.0
(ex Alert-78)							
BARGARTH * (IRL)	1960	161	28,90	7,17	3,81	1260	17.0
GW 214 (GBR)	1975	24	15,40	5,00	1,70	450	5.0
INGLEBY CROSS (GBR)	1967	139	26,52	7,68	3,30	1200	15.0
(ex Anglian Man-95, Gunnet-90)							

Towage and marine services at Waterford
* BARGARTH reported sold to UK owners in February 2009

IRISH MAINPORT GROUP
Monahan Road, Cork, Republic of Ireland
Tel : +353 21 4317900   Fax : +353 21 4318381
E-mail : info@mainport.ie
Website : www.mainport.ie
Livery - Dark blue hull with white housing
Operated by Celtic Tugs Ltd

CELTIC BANNER (IRL)	1982	282	32,85	9,50	3,23	3400	45.41
(ex Take Maru No. 78-00, Mikawa Maru-98)							
CELTIC ISLE (IRL)	1986	411	34,20	10,50	4,78	4000	53.60
(ex Tai O-00)							
CELTIC REBEL (IRL)	1984	198	31,20	9,01	4,09	3400	48.44
(ex Take Maru No. 71-00)							

Towage and offshore services on the River Shannon and in the Irish Sea
Part of Mainport Group

ISLAND SHIPPING
Dispensary Lane, Wicklow, County Wicklow, Republic of Ireland
Tel : +353 40 461623   Fax : 353 40 466063
E-mail : info@islandshipping.ie
Website : www.islandshipping.ie
ISLAND

RETRIEVER (ANT)	2008	175	24,00	8,00	2,70	1450	21.0
HUSKY (IRL)	1986	72	21,00	6,00	1,80	804	10.0

Towage, salvage, dredging support, offshore windfarm support, hydrographic survey services throughtout Ireland and the UK

LASTAMARA TEO
New Docks, Galway, County Galway, Republic of Ireland
Tel : +353 91 568942   Fax : +353 91 568951
E-mail : info@lastmarateo.com
Website : www.lastamarateo.com

TROJAN (IRL)	1976	33	14,17	4,57	2,37	460	5.5

(ex Conservative-03, Junior-93)

Marine services servicing the Aran Islands

LEE TOWAGE LTD
5 Victoria Estate, Carrignfoy, Cobh, County Cork ,Republic of Ireland
Tel/Fax : +353 21 4813034
E-mail : leetowage@go.free.indigo.ie
Website : www.ostensjo.no
Livery - Navy blue hull with light blue housing, navy blue funnel with white band and company logo

ALEX (IRL)	1995	397	30,80	11,14	4,78	4004	50.0

(ex Atlantic Fir-97)

Towage at Cobh and Whitegate

Part of Østensjø Rederei A/S

MARINE BLAST LTD
Cartown, Ballymackenny, Drogheda, County Louth, Republic of Ireland
Tel : +353 41 9822459   Fax : +353 41 9822931

MARIE JOSE (GBR)	1974		14,15	4,55	1,70	365	4.1

(ex Pushycat)

Marine and underwater services on the east coast of Ireland

The ALEX at Cobh on 15 August 2004.

(Simon Smith)

MARINE TRANSPORT SERVICES LTD
Atlantic Quay, Cobh, County Cork, Republic of Ireland
Tel : +353 21 811485   Fax : +353 21 21812645
E-mail : eoin@scottcobh.ie
Website : www.scottcobh.ie
Livery - Red hull with white housing and light blue funnel with red trim

AGHADA (IRL)	1979		10,74	3,50	1,37	127	
BREEDBANK (IRL)	1969	274	33,95	9,22	4,60	3000	30.0
(ex Canada-79, Breedbank-76)							
OYSTER BANK (IRL)	1960	170	27,50	8,00	4,00	1360	17.0
(ex Oyster Bay-95, Totland-93, Europabank-82, Europa-73)							
SALEEN (IRL)	1979		10,74	3,50	1,37	127	
SHEILA (IRL)	1979		10,74	3,50	1,37	127	
SPITBANK (IRL)	1982		12,80	3,90	1,60	220	2.5
TURBOTBANK (IRL)	1982		12,80	3,90	1,60	220	2.5

Towage services at Cobh and Cork
Part of the Doyle Shipping Group, Cobh

SHANNON FOYNES PORT COMPANY
Harbour Office, Foynes, County Limerick, Republic of Ireland
Tel : +353 69 73100   Fax : +353 69 65142
E-mail : info@sfpc.ie
Website : www.sfpc.ie

SHANNON 1 (IRL)	2008	18,85	8,36	1,89	960	13.2

Marine services on the Shannon Estuary

SHANNON WORKBOATS LIMITED
Boolaglas Askeaton, County Limerick, Republic of Ireland
Tel : +353 61 392419   Fax : +353 61 392410
E-mail : mjkehoe@eircom.net

TORBAY ENDEAVOUR	1975	27	15,75	4,90	2,70	295	4.5

Marine services on the Shannon estuary
Towage services on the east coast of Ireland and charter work

SINBAD MARINE SERVICES LTD
Shore Road, Killybegs, County Donegal, Republic of Ireland
Tel : +353 74 973 1417   Fax : +353 74 973 1864
E-mail : noel@sinbadmarine.com
Website : www.sinbadmarine.com
Livery - Blue hull with white housing and wheelhouse

CARRON (IRL)	1979	225	28,45	8,92	2,90	2190	24.0

The CARRON had only recently been acquired by Sinbad Marine Services when noted in James Watt Dock, Greenock, on 5 October 2008.

(Dominic McCall)

COASTAL CAT (IRL)	2007	17	10,00	4,40	1,00	360	3.0
NOMAD (IRL)	1972	91	23,70	7,00	2,62	565	8.5
(ex Duke of Normandy-05)							
SMS							
SHOALBUSTER (GBR)	2008	212	26,02	9,10	2,60	2200	30.0

Towage and marine services in the Killybegs area; also coastal towage

The SMS SHOALBUSTER of Sinbad Marine Services arrives at Great Yarmouth on 18 May 2008.

(Ashley Hunn)

SOUTH EAST TUG SERVICES LTD
(CATHERINE O'HANLON-CANTRELL)
19 Otteran Place, South Parade, Waterford, County Waterford, Republic of Ireland
Tel : +353 51 852819
E-mail : setugs@eircom.net

| TRAMONTANE (GBR) | 1972 | 263 | 31,63 | 9,25 | 2,99 | 2500 | 30.0 |

(ex Marseillais 16-89)

Towage services around the east coast of Ireland, also charter work

UNKNOWN OWNERS

| POOLBEG (IRL) | 1979 | 20 | 14,38 | 4,17 | | |
| ZAR IV (IRL) | 1914 | 25 | 17,53 | 5,24 | 2,25 | 430 |

TUGS - GIBRALTAR

GIBRALTAR UNDERWATER CONTRACTORS LTD (GIBUNCO)
Waterport House, PO Box 51, Waterport, Gibraltar
Tel : +350 70454   Fax : +350 79065
Livery - Black hull with buff housing and wheelhouse

SEALYHAM	(GIB)	1967	152	28,67	7,39	3,66	1320	16.1

Marine services at Gibraltar

M H BLAND & CO LTD
Cloister Building, Market Lane, PO Box 554, Gibraltar
Tel : +350 79478   Fax : +350 71608
E-mail : shipping@mhbland.gi
Website : www.mhbland.com
Livery - Black hull with mustard housing and black funnels with red stripe

FLYFISH	(GIB)	1969	77	22,10	6,25	2,50	495	6.0

(ex Edith-95)

Towage and marine services at Gibraltar

T P TOWAGE CO LTD
PO Box 801, Berth 11, North Mole, Gibraltar
Tel : +350 41912   Fax : +350 43050
E-mail : towage@gibnyney.gi
Website : www.tptowage.com
Livery - Black hull with buff housing and wheelhouse

EGERTON	(GBR)	1969	193	29,01	8,51	4,50	1500	18.0
SUN SWALE	(GBR)	1968	195	29,01	8,51	4,50	1430	18.0
WELLINGTON	(GBR)	1980	282	30,21	9,45	4,40	2640	32.0

(ex Subtil-91) — EGERTON
(ex Clairvoyant-81) — SUN SWALE
(ex Smit Canada-08, Canada-07) — WELLINGTON

Towage services at Gibraltar

The EGERTON is seen at Gibraltar on 8 November 2008.

(Simon Smith)

INDEX OF VESSEL NAMES

Current names are in CAPITAL letters, previous names are in lower case.

Name	No.	Name	No.	Name	No.
Broodbank	32	CHIEFTON	68	DEA CONQUEROR	13
BRUISER	36	Chiefton	28	Dea Fighter	23
BUE Canna	23	CHIMERA	59	DEA HERCULES	13
BUE Iona	23	CHRISTINE	29	Dea Hunter	23
BUE Islay	23	CITADEL	5	DEA LINGUE	13
BUE Lismore	23	Cito 1	59	Dea Mariner	23
BUE Mull	24	City of Aberdeen	15	DEA OCEAN	13
BUE Raasay	24	Clairvoyant	102	DEA ODYSSEY	13
BUE Stronsay	16	Cleveland Cross	80	Dea Olympian	24
BUE Tiree	24	Cleveland Endeavour	81	Dea Patrol	24
BUE Westray	15	CLIFTON	30	DEA PILOT	13
Bugsier 29	40	Clonmel	94	Dea Prince	24
Burnhaven	15	CLUAIN TARBH	97	DEA PROTECTOR	13
Bustler	73	Clutha	67	Dea Ranger	24
Butjadingen	60	CLWYD SUPPORTER	8	DEA SAILOR	13
C M KURIK	96	COASTAL CAT	100	DEA SCOUT	13
C M WULF	96	COATHAM CROSS	81	DEA SEARCHER	13
Caledonia Master	23	Cobh	54	DEA SEEKER	13
CALEDONIAN VANGUARD	5	Cobham	84	DEA SERVER	13
CALEDONIAN VICTORY	5	Cole Tide	24	Dea Signal	24
CALEDONIAN VIGILANCE	5	Collie	89	Dea Siren	24
CALEDONIAN VISION	5	COLLIE T	89	Dea Sound	24
Cam Defender	22	Collingwood	75	Dea Supplier	24
Cam Protector	24	Comar	55	DEA SUPPORTER	13
Cam Ranger	23	Comet	26	Dea Surveyor	24
Cam Sentinel	23	Condor	48	DEA ZEUS	13
Cam Supporter	24	Condor IX	48	Deben	44
Cam Vedette	24	CONFIDENCE	38	DEBORAH	28
Cam Viper	24	Conservative	98	DEERHOUND	71
Cam Viscount	17	CONSERVATOR	55	Deft	85
Campaigner	95	Coral	23	DEIDRE	89
Canada (1969)	99	Coral Sea 2	3	DEILGINIS	97
Canada (1980)	102	Corella	4	DEIRDRE McLOUGHLIN	62
Canmar Teal	13	CORRINGHAM	89	DENIS MURPHY	96
Canmar Widgeon	13	Corvin	61	DERWENT	39
CANNING	87	COULMORE	58	Dexterous	73
Capable	73	CRAMOND	89	Dextrous	84
Cariboo	11	Cruiser	94	DH Charlie	61
CAROL JAMES	33	Cubow	65	DHB DAUNTLESS	41
Carraig Dubh	60	CULTRA	89	DHB DOUGHTY	41
CARRICKFERGUS	88	CUMBRAE	67	Diamante	93
CARRON	100	Curlew	89	Diana	36
Caspar C	44	Cyclop	26	DIDO	29
CASPIAN PRIDE	5	DA McCann	27	DMS Eagle	74
CASTLE	5	DAISY DOARDO	71	DMS Heron	64
CASTLE POINT	89	DALEGARTH	85	Docat 3	48
CAVA LASS	95	Dalegarth	95	DOCKMAN	94
CELTIC BANNER	97	Dalmatian	70	Dockman	94
CELTIC ISLE	97	DALMENY	89	Dogancay X	61
CELTIC REBEL	97	DANCHA	43	Dogancay XIII	61
Celtic Warrior	87	Dancha	43	Dogancay XIV	61
Cement 7	32	DANIEL ADAMSON	40	DONNA	67
CENTRICA PRIDE	3	Danielle	71	Donna McLoughlin	67
Chain Supplier	23	Daphne	89	Doris	65
CHALLENGE	43	Daphne B	89	Doris K	65
CHALLENGER OF LEITH	37	DAVID ANDREWS	72	Dorothy	34
Champion	83	DAVID McLOUGHLIN	62	Drive Supporter	24
CHARLES PLANE	45	Dawn Patrol	3	Droit de Parole	11
CHARLIGHT	90	Dawn Shore	4	Drot	15
CHARLOC	94	Dawn Sky	4	DTS Seal	46
Charlock	94	DEA ARGOSY	13	Duchess	49
CHATEAU THIEREY	95	DEA CHALLENGER	13	DUKE OF NORMANDY	55
Chek Chau	82	DEA CHAMPION	13	Duke of Normandy	100
Cherry	35	Dea Chancellor	23	Dulas Island	53
CHIEF	28	DEA CLIPPER	13	Dunelm	94
Chief	28	Dea Commander	23	DUNTER	80

Name	No.	Name	No.	Name	No.
Durdham	32	FARSET OF BELFAST	45	GRAEMSAY LASS	88
Dutch Pearl	75	FEARNOUGHT	78	GRAMPIAN CAVALIER	14
Edda Atlantic	17	Felicity	29	GRAMPIAN COMMANDER	14
EDDA FRAM	7	FELIX TOW	40	GRAMPIAN CONQUEROR	14
Edda Sprite	18	Felix-Tow	40	GRAMPIAN CONQUEST	14
Edith	102	FENLANDER	45	GRAMPIAN CONTENDER	14
Eduard	30	Fiat Voluntas XIX	48	GRAMPIAN CORSAIR	14
Eerland 4	48	FIDRA	46	GRAMPIAN COURAGEOUS	14
EGERTON	102	FIERY CROSS	81	GRAMPIAN CRUSADER	14
EILEEN	45	Filip	28	GRAMPIAN DEE	15
EINAR	67	FIONA	94	GRAMPIAN DEFENDER	15
Eldergarth	85	FLAT HOLM	37	GRAMPIAN EXPLORER	15
Elena B	65	Flat Holm	37	GRAMPIAN FALCON	15
ELKHOUND	71	FLYFISH	102	GRAMPIAN FAME	15
ELSA	80	Flying Demon	46	GRAMPIAN FRONTIER	15
Emerald Bas	18	Flying Duck	95	GRAMPIAN GUARDIAN	15
Emerald Sprite	18	FLYING SCUD	69	Grampian Guardian	15
EMS Express	57	FLYING SPINDRIFT	84	GRAMPIAN HAVEN	15
En Avant 9	32	Forceful	74	GRAMPIAN HIGHLANDER	15
En Avant II	80	Fort Reliance	11	GRAMPIAN HUNTER	15
ENBANK	95	FORTH	80	GRAMPIAN ORCADES	16
Eness	46	Forth (1964)	46	GRAMPIAN OSPREY	16
ENGLISHMAN	77	Forth (1979)	84	GRAMPIAN OTTER	16
ERLEND	67	Forth (1967)	94	GRAMPIAN PIONEER	16
Essex Service	3	FORTH BOXER	32	GRAMPIAN PRIDE	16
Essex Shore	3	FORTH CONSTRUCTOR	32	GRAMPIAN PRINCE	16
Estay Tide	24	FORTH DRUMMER	32	GRAMPIAN PROTECTOR	16
ESTE	60	Forth Engineer	74	GRAMPIAN RANGER	16
Eston Cross	84	FORTH FIGHTER	32	GRAMPIAN SPRITE	16
ESVAGT CAPELLA	7	FORTH HUNTER	32	GRAMPIAN STAR	16
ESVAGT DEE	7	Forth Inspector	74	GRAMPIAN SURVEYOR	16
ESVAGT DON	8	FORTH JOUSTER	32	GRAMPIAN TALISMAN	16
ESVAGT OBSERVER	8	FORTH SENTINEL	32	GRAMPIAN VENTURE	16
ESVAGT SUPPORTER	8	FORTRESS	5	Gray Delta	29
Europa	99	Foylegarth	95	Gray Echo	38
Europabank	99	Foylemore	95	GRAY JUMBO	85
Evelene Brodstone	57	FREIGHT ENDEAVOUR	41	GRAY MAMMOTH	44
F. D. INCREDIBLE	10	FREIGHT MOVER	75	GRAY SALVOR	44
F. D. INVINCIBLE	10	FRISTON DOWN	48	GRAY TEST	44
F. D. IRRESISTIBLE	10	Fuji Maru	56	GRAY VIXEN	44
F. D. RELIABLE	10	FURNESS ABBEY	28	Greatham Cross	88
FAIR MAID OF PERTH	68	G-WIZ	69	GREEN LONDON	49
Fairplay 10	65	G.W. 226	69	Grey Lash	41
Faithful	74	Gael Venture	71	Gryphaea	4
FALCONBROOK	44	Gael Vision	59	Guarne	65
Falderntor	24	Ganges	58	Gunnet	97
Falgarth	63	GARGANO	11	Gurroung	83
Far Baronet	23	GARNOCK	71	Gute Salvor	23
Far Centurion	6	GARRY GRAY	94	GUY JAMES	33
Far Crusader	6	Gary Gray	94	GW 94	49
FAR GRIMSHADER	8	GARY JAMES	33	GW 108	34
Far Malin	10	Geeste	60	GW 214	97
FAR SABRE	8	Gemsar	32	Gwendoline	73
Far Scandia	8	General I	90	GWENDOLINE P	73
FAR SCIMITAR	8	General V	44	Hadja	24
FAR SCOTIA	8	GENERAL VIII	39	Hakakuni Maru	87
Far Searcher (1975)	18	GENERAL IX	90	Haki	36
Far Searcher (1985)	23	GERRY O'SULLIVAN	96	Hallarklettur	24
FAR SERVICE	8	GILLIAN KNIGHT	41	Hallgarth	26
Far Sky	16	GLENESK	55	Hamilton Piper	14
FAR SPIRIT	8	Glenesk	62	Hamilton Piper 1	14
Far Spirit	17	GLUVIAS	94	HARALD	67
FAR STRIDER	8	Gnupur	24	Harvest Reaper III	58
FAR SUPERIOR	8	GOLIATH	49	Hauler	48
FAR SUPPLIER	8	GP America	48	HAULIER	48
FAR SUPPORTER	8	GPS ANGLIA	48	Haulier	48

HAVEN HORNBILL	51	IBERIA	48	Kenry	95
Havila Clever	17	IBEX	78	KENT	78
Havila Sea	18	Ibis Five	3	Kentonvale Star	13
Havila Searcher	18	Ibis Six	13	KERNE	65
Havila Sky	18	Ibis Two	23	KESSOCK	57
Havila Star	18	Ierland	49	Kestrel (1983)	83
Havila Sun	18	Iide Maru	56	Kestrel (1985)	85
Havila Tern	18	Impetus	74	Kestrel Venture	71
Havila Tigris	17	IMPULSE	58	KEVERNE	56
HD 91	64	Impulse	74	KIERA G	65
Heco	80	Inchcolm	71	Kiklop	26
HECTOR READ	94	Independent II	48	Kilp	60
HEGRIE	33	Indus	64	Kim	18
HERBERT BALLAM	69	INGE	60	Kincraig	77
Herbert Crampin	91	INGLEBY CROSS	97	KINDEACE	56
Herman	52	INTREPID B	58	KINGDOM OF FIFE	5
Herman Jr	32	IONIA (1956)	48	Kinghow	52
HERMAN SR	49	IONIA (1960)	94	KINGSTON	49
HERMES	28	Ionia	94	Kingston Buci	28
HIGHLAND BUGLER	8	IRISHMAN	77	KINGSTON LACY	28
HIGHLAND CHAMPION	8	ISABEL	71	Kinnel	52
HIGHLAND CITADEL	9	Island Pride	5	KINTORE	56
HIGHLAND COURAGE	9	ISLAND RETRIEVER	98	KIRKWALL BAY	67
HIGHLAND DRUMMER	9	ISLAY	5	Kiso Maru	70
HIGHLAND EAGLE	9	Iwashima Maru	84	KNAB	58
HIGHLAND ENDURANCE	9	JACK JAMES	33	Knab	60
HIGHLAND FORTRESS	9	JADI	60	KNAP	60
HIGHLAND LEGEND	9	Jagima	22	KNIGHTON	49
HIGHLAND MONARCH	9	JAMES WARD	94	Komet	26
HIGHLAND NAVIGATOR	9	Jan Goedkoop Jnr	60	Kongsholm	23
HIGHLAND PIONEER	9	JANET JAMES	33	Kronbas	17
HIGHLAND PIPER	9	JANETTE B	49	Kuroshio	83
Highland Piper	23	Jason	23	KUTARI	57
Highland Piper 1	23	Java Seal	4	Lady Alma	81
HIGHLAND PRESTIGE	9	Jaycee	94	Lady Anya	83
HIGHLAND PRIDE	10	Jean Raby	63	Lady Brenda	83
HIGHLAND ROVER	10	Jenny	48	LADY CECILIA	83
HIGHLAND SPIRIT	10	JESSICA S	36	Lady Constance	81
HIGHLAND SPRITE	10	JESSIE K	80	Lady Elizabeth	81
HIGHLAND STAR	10	Jim Higgs	49	Lady Emma	82
HIGHLAND TRADER	10	JOAN	29	Lady Emma H	82
HIGHLAND VALOUR	10	JOHN KING	32	Lady Josephine	82
HIGHLAND WARRIOR	10	Johnshaven	16	Lady Kathleen	82
Hispania	55	JOSINE	32	Lady Laura (1967)	32
HOFLAND	94	JULIA M	46	Lady Laura (2001)	82
Holmgarth	46	Jumbo	30	Lady Madeleine	83
Honzan Maru	77	Junior	98	Lady Moira	82
HOPETOUN	89	JURA	5	Lady Morag	83
Hornbeck Baronet	23	KAMSAR	29	Lady Sarah	84
Hornbeck Coral	23	Kapelle	48	LADY STEPHANIE	81
Hornbeck Sapphire	23	Kapitan Engler	49	LADY SUSAN	83
Hornbeck Sceptre	24	Kapitän Engler	49	Lady Sybil	65
Hornbeck Searcher	23	Kara Seal	13	Lady Vivien	3
Hornbeck Supreme	24	Karet	65	Lagan	57
Hornbeck Swan	5	Karin S	93	Laggan	84
HORTON	27	Karnfjord	32	Landry Tide	13
Horton	27	Kaskazi	23	LASHETTE	41
HT BLADE	44	KATHLEEN	62	LAURA M	46
HT CUTLASS	84	Kathy M	65	LB1	45
HT Sabre	81	Katliz	61	Le Gabion	89
HT SCIMITAR	85	KEBISTER	58	LEANNE McLOUGHLIN	62
HT Sword	82	Keelman	94	Lehnkering 11	71
Humber Sentinel	32	KENLEY	57	Lehnkering 108	71
HUSKY	98	Kenley	83	LESLENE	60
Husky	74	KENNET	57	LESLEY M	46
HYDRONAUT	54	Kenneth G	65	LIBRA STAR	70

.ighterman	94	MARIE JOSE	98	M.S.C. Dido	29
.ILAH	63	MARINECO ASHANTI	60	M.S.C. Sceptre	49
.INFORD	41	MARINECO HATHI	60	M.S.C. VICEROY	35
.ingo	39	MARINECO INDIA	60	M.S.C. VICTORY	35
.ingue	13	Marineco Seeonee	36	M.S.C. VIKING	35
.ITTLE KIRKBY	27	Marineco Sheerkhan	89	M.S.C. VOLANT	35
.ITTLE SHIFTA	27	MARINECO TOOMAI	60	MTS INDUS	64
.ITTLE SHUVA	27	Mariska V	61	MTS TAKTOW	64
.LANDDWYN ISLAND	52	Marker II	47	MTS VALIANT	64
.och Grimshader	8	Marpol Fighter	10	MTS VALID	64
.och Shiel	36	Marsea One	13	MTS VALOUR	64
.och Shuna	17	Marseillais 16	101	MTS VENGEANCE	65
.ofottral III	24	MARY	41	MTS VICTORY	65
.ONAN	57	MARY M	46	MTS VIXEN	65
.ORD DEVONPORT	47	MARY-ANN McLOUGHLIN	62	MTS VULCAN	65
.ord Ritchie	49	Mastodon	13	Multrasalvor 2	96
.ord Waverley	47	Maura	62	MULTRATUG 5	56
.otus	71	MAXIMUS	94	Munkholmen	59
.OUISE B	94	MAYFLOWER	32	MURIA	48
.owgarth	45	MCL1	46	Nagato Maru	77
.owland Pioneer	9	MCS AILSA	61	NAPIA	48
.uvly Jubbly	94	MCS ALIX	61	Nat 113	48
.yndhurst	83	MCS ANIE	61	Needham Tide	13
.ynn Pelham	13	MCS ANNEKE	61	Neftegaz-12	8
.lack	57	MCS ELLY	61	NEFTEGAZ-62	6
.IADELEN	95	MCS HEATHER	61	Neptune	48
.IAERSK ADVANCER	12	MCS IRIS	61	NERCHA	6
.IAERSK ASSERTER	12	MCS LENIE	61	NEW ROSS 1	34
.IAERSK BEATER	12	MCS Lenie	74	Nice Tango	5
.IAERSK CUTTER	12	MCS MARLENE	61	Niger	36
.Iaersk Dee	7	MCS Menno	46	Nimble	74
.Iaersk Don	8	MCS NIKKI	61	NIPASHORE	29
.IAERSK FINDER	12	MCS Nikki	36	NOBLEMAN	6
.IAERSK HANDLER	12	Medway	36	NOLEEN McLOUGHLIN	62
.Iaersk Handler	6	MEDWAY OTTER	62	NOMAD	100
.IAERSK HELPER	12	MEECHING	94	Noordster 7	48
.Iaersk Leader	3	MEGAN M	46	Nor Truck	23
.Iaersk Logger (1987)	11	Melton	83	Norah	53
.Iaersk Logger (1976)	3	MERANO	63	NORE CHALLENGER	65
.IAERSK MARINER	12	Mercedes II	63	NORE COMMODORE	65
.Iaersk Pacer	15	MERIT	39	NORE SWALE	65
.Iaersk Piper	4	MERLIN (1975)	59	NORE TRITON	65
.IAERSK RETRIEVER	12	MERLIN (1964)	64	Norfolk Service	4
.IAERSK RIDER	12	Mersey One	80	Norfolk Shore	4
.IAERSK ROVER	12	MERSINA	39	NORMAN	77
.IAERSK SEARCHER	12	MICHAEL FRANCIS	92	NORMAND AURORA	20
.IAERSK SERVER	12	MICHAEL McLOUGHLIN	62	Normand Carrier	13
.IAERSK SHIPPER	12	Midgard I	60	NORMAND CLIPPER	20
.IAERSK SUPPORTER	12	Mikawa Maru	97	Normand Conger	23
.Iaersk Supporter (1971)	5	MILLGARTH	85	NORMAND CUTTER	20
.Iaersk Supporter (1983)	6	Misr Gulf VII	6	Normand Engineer	23
.Iaersk Tanis	3	Mohamed	3	NORMAND FLIPPER	20
.Iaersk Tanta	3	Mona Viking	22	Normand Gard	23
.Iaersk Trinity	6	MONARCH M	31	Normand Hunter	23
.Iaersk Worker	4	MONOGIRL	38	NORMAND INSTALLER	20
.Iagdalena	71	MONOGIRL 2	38	NORMAND JARL	20
.IAGGIE M	46	Montenovo	87	NORMAND MARINER	20
.Iahone Bay	6	Moon Lady	3	NORMAND MJOLNE	21
.IAINPORT ASH	11	MORAG M	46	NORMAND NEPTUN	21
.IAINPORT ELM	11	Moray	11	Normand Ondur	24
.IAINPORT OAK	11	MORGAWR	46	NORMAND PIONEER	21
.Iansal	3	MOURNE SHORE	40	Normand Providence	15
.Iargaret Barry	47	MOURNE VALLEY	40	Normand Skipper	24
.Iargaret Isobell	54	M.S.C. DAINTY	59	NORMAND TONJER	21
.IARIA McLOUGHLIN	62	M.S.C. DAWN	59	NORMAND VESTER	21
.IARIANA K	80	M.S.C. Deborah	28	Normand Vibran	23

Name	No.	Name	No.	Name	No.
Norse Tide	24	PEARL	11	PUTFORD WORKER	4
Norseman	6	PENDENNICK	94	R 5	18
Norskjell	10	Peng	82	RACIA	48
Norskjell Nor	10	Peng Chau	82	Raiti	17
North Breeze	18	PENLEATH	46	Ralph Brocklebank	40
North Prince	24	PEP	53	Rathgarth	95
North Safe	16	PERCUIL	26	RECRUIT	39
NORTH STACK	52	Peter Leigh	32	RED COUNTESS	89
NORTHERN CANYON	21	Petromar General	13	RED DOLPHIN	77
NORTHERN CHASER	21	PHENIX	78	Red Duchess	49
NORTHERN FALCON	43	Phoenix (1955)	48	RED EMPRESS	89
NORTHERN MARINER	22	Phoenix (1943)	49	Red Sea Trader	15
NORTHERN QUEEN	22	PHOENIX CROSS	81	RED WOLF	77
NORTHERN SUPPORTER	22	Pieter Goedkoop	48	Redbridge	83
Northern Viking	17	PIONEER (1955)	59	Redcliffe	82
NORTON CROSS	87	PIONEER (1967)	65	REGAIN	39
NOVA	3	Placard	41	Regard	47
Nova Service	3	Placate	53	REGARDER	47
Nova Shore	3	Placer	41	REGIS 2	37
Nuna	23	Plan Searcher	18	Rem Searcher	18
OAKGARTH	86	Plankton	41	Rembertiturm	18
OCEAN CLEVER	17	PLANTER	71	Remo	77
Ocean Coral	23	PLASHY	94	Repulse	39
OCEAN FIGHTER	16	Plausible	75	Request	63
OCEAN NESS	17	Plym Echo	38	Rescue Kim	18
Ocean Pilot	23	Polar Fjord	15	Rescue Tern	18
OCEAN PRINCE	16	Polgarth	94	Resolute	70
Ocean Range	18	POLMEAR	55	RESOLUTE LADY	70
OCEAN SEARCHER	18	POOLBEG	101	RESOLVE	39
Ocean Service	24	PORTGARTH	84	RETAINER	39
OCEAN SKY	16	Portnahaven	15	REVENGE	47
OCEAN SPEY	18	PORTOSALVO	11	RICHARD HART	48
OCEAN SPIRIT	17	PORTREE GIRL	49	Rig Mate	3
OCEAN SPRITE	18	PORTWEY	79	RIVERMAN	94
OCEAN SUN	18	Powerful	74	Riverman	94
OCEAN SUPPLIER	6	PRENTICE	29	RM Margaux	48
OCEAN SUPPORTER	6	Prestwick	65	Rollanes	16
OCEAN SWAN	18	Pride	32	ROMAN	6
OCEAN SWIFT	18	PRIMROSE	41	ROSEBERRY CROSS	80
OCEAN TERN	18	PRINCE ROCK	35	Rossend	94
OCEAN VIKING	17	PRINCETON	49	Rossinant	13
OCEAN VISCOUNT	17	Protector	64	ROSSLYN	94
OCEAN WEST	17	PUFFIN ISLAND	52	ROWANGARTH	81
Oceanic Pioneer	9	Pullman	70	Royal	23
Oddstein	24	Pushdale H	35	RUFUS CASTLE	70
ODS Manta	23	Pushycat	98	Rupelmonde	48
Offshore Hunter	23	PUTFORD ACHATES	3	RYSA LASS	95
Oil Randan	60	PUTFORD ACHILLES	3	S.B. 1	36
Oil Retainer	39	PUTFORD AJAX	3	Sabrina	46
OLIVER	41	PUTFORD APOLLO	3	Safe Tango	5
OLIVER FELIX	94	PUTFORD ARIES	3	Safe Truck (1976)	4
Oliver Felix	94	PUTFORD ARTEMIS	3	Safe Truck (1996)	10
Olympic Supplier	6	PUTFORD ATHENA	3	SALEEN	99
Omar	55	PUTFORD ENTERPRISE	3	Salgado	24
ORMESBY CROSS	81	PUTFORD GUARDIAN	3	SALLY	46
ORSETT	41	PUTFORD JAGUAR	3	Salud	36
OSPREY FIGHTER	67	PUTFORD PROTECTOR	3	Salvageman	55
OTTERBANK	58	PUTFORD PROVIDER	3	Sandhaven	16
OXCAR	46	PUTFORD PUFFIN	3	SANDSFOOT CASTLE	70
OYSTER BANK	99	PUTFORD ROVER	4	Sandsfoot Castle	65
Oyster Bay	99	PUTFORD SHORE	4	Sape	23
Pan Salvor	23	PUTFORD SKY	4	Sapphire Tide	23
Pan Searcher	18	PUTFORD TERMINATOR	4	Sapucaia	24
Pan Sky	16	PUTFORD TRADER	4	Sarah C	29
Patmore	59	PUTFORD VIKING	4	SARAH D	81
PAUL H	29	PUTFORD VOYAGER	4	SARAH GREY	36

Name	No.	Name	No.	Name	No.
SARAH McLOUGHLIN	62	Sea Worker	22	SMIT COLLINGWOOD	75
SARTOR	17	Seaboard Coral	23	SMIT DONAU	75
SBS CIRRUS	18	Seaboard Sapphire	23	SMIT FOWLER	76
SBS NIMBUS	18	Seaboard Sceptre	24	SMIT LIVERPOOL	75
SBS STRATUS	18	Seaboard Supreme	24	Smit Spanje	48
SBS TEMPEST	18	Seaboard Swan	5	SMIT WATERLOO	75
SBS TORRENT	18	Seacor Argosy	13	SMIT YOUNG	76
SBS TYPHOON	18	Seacor Easterner	3	Smit-Lloyd 25	11
Sceptre Tide	24	Seacor Excellence	3	Smit-Lloyd 31	11
Schnoorturm	6	Seaforth Baronet	23	Smit-Lloyd 32	11
Scorcher	94	Seaforth Centurion	6	Smit-Lloyd 41	13
Scotscraig	95	Seaforth Crusader	6	Smit-Lloyd 57	13
Scott Guardian	23	SEAHAM PRIDE	72	Smit-Lloyd 71	13
Scott Protector	13	Seahorse	92	Smit-Lloyd 73	13
SD ADEPT	73	SEAHORSE SUPPORTER	11	Smit-Lloyd Sound	24
SD ATLAS	73	SEAL CARR	46	SMS SHOALBUSTER	100
SD BOUNTIFUL	73	Sealion Columbia	17	Smudge	43
SD BUSTLER	73	SEALYHAM	102	Snatchette	27
SD CAPABLE	73	Seamaid	68	Somme	94
SD CAREFUL	73	SEAPORT ALPHA	91	SOWENA	75
SD CATHERINE	73	Searcher	23	Spaniel	74
SD CHRISTINE	73	Seaway Jura	4	SPEEDWELL	41
SD DEBORAH	73	SEFTON SUPPORTER	10	SPITBANK	99
SD DEPENDABLE	73	SEIONT IV	34	Sprite	18
SD DEXTEROUS	73	Selco Supply 1	3	SPURN HAVEN II	6
SD EILEEN	73	Selco Supply II	13	ST BUDOC	95
SD EMILY	74	Senho Maru	86	ST DAVID	79
SD ENGINEER	74	Sentinel Cathinka	23	St David	24
SD FAITHFUL	74	Sentinel Maria	23	St Gluvias	94
SD FLORENCE	74	Sentinel Teresa	24	ST MARGARET	71
SD FORCEFUL	74	Sentry Hemne	24	St Mawes	94
SD FRANCES	74	SERVICEMAN	77	ST PIRAN (1979)	26
SD GENEVIEVE	74	Severn Mariner	3	ST PIRAN (1960)	95
SD GEORGINA	74	SHALDER	80	STACKGARTH	84
SD HELEN	74	Shalldo	95	Stad Flex	10
SD HERCULES	74	SHANNON	85	Stad Scandia	8
SD HUSKY	74	SHANNON 1	99	Stad Scandia	15
SD IMPETUS	74	SHANNON ESTUARY I	95	Stad Sky	16
SD IMPULSE	74	Sheepdog	74	Stad Spirit	17
SD INDEPENDENT	74	SHEERKHAN	89	Stad Supplier	16
SD INDULGENT	74	SHEILA	99	Stamford Brook	94
SD INSPECTOR	74	Shinano Maru	77	Standby Pioneer	16
SD JUPITER	74	Shoalbuster	96	Standby Pride	16
SD KITTY	74	Shorne	85	Standby Protector	16
SD KYLE OF LOCHALSH	74	SHOVETTE	41	STANECHAKKER	80
SD LESLEY	74	SHROVE	58	STANFORD	89
SD MARS	74	Siddis Mariner	3	Star Altair	3
SD MYRTLE	74	Siggbas	17	Star Aries	3
SD NAVIGATOR	74	Silverbeam	63	Star Capella	3
SD NIMBLE	74	SILVERBEAM	63	Star Pegasus	4
SD POWERFUL	74	SIR AUBREY	47	Star Spica	24
SD RAASAY	74	Sir Aubrey	47	Star Vega	3
SD RELIABLE	74	Sir Bevois	84	Starmi	13
SD RESOURCEFUL	74	Sira Supporter	24	STATESMAN	6
SD SHEEPDOG	74	SKANDI BARRA	6	Stedingen	60
SD SPANIEL	74	SKANDI CARLA	7	Stella Salvator	23
SD SUZANNE	74	SKANDI FOULA	7	STENLAND	95
SD TILLY	74	SKANDI RONA	7	STEVEN B	30
SEA CHALLENGE II	30	Skelton Cross	89	Stint	35
SEA GRIFFON	94	Skjelsvik	59	Stirling Altair	3
Sea Guardian	22	Smit Amerika	90	Stirling Aries	3
SEA HELPER	26	SMIT ARROL	76	Stirling Capella	3
Sea Sapphire	23	SMIT BAKER	76	Stirling Dee	4
Sea Serv Osprey	16	SMIT BARBADOS	75	Stirling Elf	16
SEA TRACTOR	65	Smit Barracuda	3	Stirling Esk	4
SEA TROJAN	51	Smit Canada	102	Stirling Imp	15

Stirling Islay	5	SVITZER MALTBY	85	TIRRICK	80
Stirling Jura	5	SVITZER MELTON	83	TNT Leopard	19
Stirling Merlin	15	SVITZER MERCIA	83	TNT Lion	19
Stirling Osprey	16	SVITZER MILFORD	87	TNT Tiger	19
Stirling Puck	16	SVITZER MOIRA	82	TOISA CONQUEROR	18
Stirling Spica	24	SVITZER MORAG	83	TOISA CORAL	19
Stirling Sprite	16	SVITZER MUSSELWICK	85	TOISA CREST	19
Stirling Tern	16	SVITZER RAMSEY	86	TOISA DARING	19
Stirling Vega	3	SVITZER REDBRIDGE	83	TOISA DAUNTLESS	19
Stoneness	46	SVITZER SARAH	84	TOISA DEFIANT	19
STOREBROR	32	SVITZER SHOTLEY	83	TOISA INDEPENDENT	19
STRATHDOON	69	SVITZER SKY	84	TOISA INTREPID	19
Strongbow	85	SVITZER STANLOW	86	TOISA INVINCIBLE	19
Subtil	102	SVITZER SUN	81	TOISA LEOPARD	19
Suffolk Conquest	23	SVITZER SUSSEX	84	TOISA LION	19
Suffolk Harvester	23	SVITZER SWORD	82	TOISA PALADIN	19
Suffolk Mariner	22	SVITZER TAKU	86	Toisa Petrel	13
Suffolk Monarch	24	SVITZER THAW	86	Toisa Plover	13
Suffolk Supporter	22	SVITZER THUNDER	86	Toisa Puffin	13
Suffolk Warrior	24	SVITZER TORNADO	86	TOISA SERENADE	19
Sun Anglia	83	SVITZER TORRENT	86	TOISA SOLITAIRE	19
Sun Mercia	83	SVITZER TRIMLEY	83	TOISA SONATA	19
Sun Prince	24	SVITZER TWISTER	86	Toisa Teal	13
Sun Surrey	83	SVITZER VALIANT	82	TOISA TIGER	19
Sun Sussex	84	SVITZER VICTORY	83	TOISA VALIANT	19
SUN SWALE	102	SVITZER WARDEN	83	TOISA VIGILANT	19
Sun Tender	18	SVITZER WATERSTON	86	TOISA VOYAGER	19
Sun Thames	82	SVITZER WATWICK	86	Toisa Widgeon	13
Sun Wrestler	6	SWAN	5	Tolo	77
Sun XXIII	47	SWIFTSTONE	88	TORBAY ENDEAVOUR	100
Sun XXIV	49	Swissco Super	75	TORBROOK	95
Sunbas	18	SWITHA LASS	88	TORCH	36
SUNCREST	47	SYLVESTER	32	Torland	8
Sunset Baronet	23	Tadami Maru	83	Torland I	8
Sunset Searcher	23	Tai O	97	Toro	95
Sunwind	47	Tai Tam	77	Totland	99
Superbe	65	Take Maru No. 71	97	TOUCHSTONE	36
Supreme	24	Take Maru No. 78	97	Toward Venture	54
SUSAN	29	Taktow 1	64	Towfish	65
SVITZER ALMA	81	TARPAN	75	TRADESMAN	77
SVITZER ANGLIA	83	TARROO USHTEY	53	Trafalgar Guardian	24
SVITZER BEVOIS	84	Taucher O. Wulf	96	TRAMONTANE	101
SVITZER BIDSTON	86	TAYRA	59	Tregarth	95
SVITZER BOOTLE	81	Tayra	59	TREGEAGLE	46
SVITZER BRENDA	83	Te Awhina	89	TRIO	67
SVITZER BRIGHTWELL	83	TEGEN	75	Trio	64
SVITZER BRISTOL	84	TEIGN C	89	Triumph Sea	23
SVITZER BRUNEL	84	TENAX	78	TROJAN	98
SVITZER CALDY	85	Tender Champion	8	TRUEMAN	77
SVITZER CONSTANCE	81	Tender Fighter	17	TS-52 Sound	24
SVITZER ELIZABETH	81	Tender Searcher	18	Tsing Yi	77
SVITZER ELLERBY	82	Tenzan	87	Tugman	94
SVITZER FERRIBY	82	Terese Marie	57	TULPAR	5
SVITZER GELLISWICK	85	Terrier	65	TURBOTBANK	99
SVITZER HARTY	83	Thelm Leigh	70	TYPHOON	4
SVITZER HAVEN	85	THOMAS F DOYLE	95	TYSTIE	80
SVITZER INTREPID	83	THORNGARTH	87	UGIE RUNNER	69
SVITZER JOSEPHINE	82	THRAX	78	UKD Flat Holm	37
SVITZER KATHLEEN	82	THUMPER	69	UKD SEAHORSE	91
SVITZER KEELBY	82	TID 43	91	UKD SEALION	91
SVITZER KILROOM	85	TID 172	79	UNICO	68
SVITZER LACEBY	83	TID 174	94	URSA	55
SVITZER LAURA	82	TID 180	32	V-RON	69
SVITZER LINDSWAY	85	Tideall	91	Valiant B	79
SVITZER MADELEINE	83	TILLY	47	VALID	95
SVITZER MALLAIG	87	TIOGA B	29	Valour	80

VANGUARD	95	VOS COMMANDER	23	WELLINGTON	102
Vanoc	90	VOS CONQUEST	23	WELSHMAN	77
Veesea	13	VOS CRUSADER	23	Wendentor	11
Veesea Pearl	11	VOS DISCOVERY	23	WENDY ANN	57
Veesea Typhoon	4	VOS EMPEROR	23	West Penguin	17
VELOX	95	VOS FIGHTER	23	West Plover	17
Ventura	6	VOS GUARDIAN	23	West Tern	18
VENTURE	71	VOS HARVESTER	23	WESTGARTH	85
Venturer	23	VOS HUNTER	23	WILANNE	93
VER	44	VOS INNOVATOR	23	WILCAT	93
VERA LOCKHART	46	VOS INSPIRER	23	WILENDEAVOUR	93
Veronica	57	VOS ISLAY	23	WILFREEDOM	92
Veronica Viking	17	VOS LISMORE	23	WILKIT	93
Vespa	57	VOS MARINER	23	William George	48
VIGOUR	35	VOS MASTER	23	WILLIAM RYAN	95
Viking	65	VOS MONARCH	24	WILLOWGARTH	87
Viking Crusader	23	VOS MULL	24	WILLPOWER	93
VIKING DEFENDER	22	VOS OLYMPIAN	24	Wimpey Seasprite	10
Viking Discovery	23	VOS PATHFINDER	23	Wimpey Seawitch	9
VIKING EXPLORER	22	VOS PATROL	24	Wira Maju	10
Viking Fighter	17	VOS PIONEER	24	WMPS SEAHORSE	92
Viking Guardian	23	VOS PRINCE	24	Wouter Johannis	64
VIKING IONA	23	VOS PROSPECTOR	24	WYEFORCE	53
Viking Islay	23	VOS PROTECTOR	24	WYEFUEL	53
Viking Mull	24	VOS RAASAY	24	Wyefuel	80
Viking Prince	16	VOS RUNNER	24	Wyeguard	52
Viking Protector	24	VOS SEEKER	24	Wyepress	29
VIKING PROVIDER	23	VOS SIGNAL	24	Wyepull	55
Viking Raasay	24	VOS SIREN	24	WYEPUSH	53
VIKING RANGER	23	VOS SOUND	24	WYETOW	53
VIKING SENTINEL	23	VOS SUPPLIER	24	WYKE CASTLE	70
Viking Tiree	24	VOS SUPPORTER	24	YARENGA	6
Viking Vedette	24	VOS SURVEYOR	24	YARM CROSS	81
Viking Viper	24	VOS TIREE	24	Yarra	46
Viking Viscount	17	VOS VEDETTE	24	Yashima	85
Vildanden	59	VOS VICTORY	24	Yenikale	73
VINCIA	48	VOS VIPER	24	YEOMAN	77
Vista	90	VOS VOYAGER	24	YEWGARTH	85
Vivien Tide	3	VOS WARRIOR	24	Yokosuka Maru No. 1	85
VOE III	29	W J Trotter	82	Yokosuka Maru No. 2	83
VOE JARL	41	Waglan	77	Zal 4	32
VOE SERVICE	41	Walborg	70	ZAR IV	101
VOE VENTURE	41	WARRIOR	90	Zeepaard (1988)	33
VOE VIKING	41	WARRIOR III	87	Zeepaard (1955)	48
Volharding 12	48	Waterloo	75	ZEEPIA	48
Volito	71	Waveney Castle	5	Zephyr	65
VOS CANNA	23	Waveney Citadel	9	Zwerver	47
VOS CHANCELLOR	23	WAVERLEY	47	Zwerver II	52

Flag abbreviations

ANT	Netherlands Antilles	ESP	Spain	NIS	Norwegian International
AZE	Azerbaijan	GIB	Gibraltar	NLD	Netherlands
BHS	Bahamas	GBR	United Kingdom	NOR	Norway
BLZ	Belize	HKG	Hong Kong	PAN	Panama
BRB	Barbados	IOM	Isle of Man	PMD	Madeira
COM	Comoros	IRL	Republic of Ireland	SKN	St Kitts & Nevis
CYM	Cayman Islands	KAZ	Kazakhstan	TKM	Turkmenistan
CYP	Cyprus	MHL	Marshall Islands	VCT	St Vincent & Grenadines
DIS	Danish International	SGP	Singapore		
DMA	Dominica	SLE	Sierra Leone		

Back cover : Several older vessels supporting offshore oil fiields have been converted on one or more occasions. The PUTFORD SKY, seen at Lowestoft on 12 February 2008, was built as a stern trawler. In 1983 she was converted to a research vessel and then in 1993 into a standby safety vessel.

(Dominic McCall)

The KINDEACE appears to be hurrying away from the storm gathering astern of her in the Clyde estuary on 28 February 2008.

(Danny Lynch)

The weather in Gibraltar seems more settled than that in the Clyde when the WELLINGTON was photographed on 8 November 2008.

(Simon Smith)